GENESIS
and
Scientific Inquiry

GENESIS
and
Scientific Inquiry

By

ALDERT VAN DER ZIEL
Electrical Engineering Department
University of Minnesota
Minneapolis, Minnesota

Publishers
T. S. DENISON & COMPANY, INC.
Minneapolis

FOREWORD

How would a distinguished scientist, who possesses positive theological convictions even though he is not a fundamentalist, interpret the opening chapters of Genesis? The pages of this volume contain an authentic answer to this interesting question.

The alert reader of Scripture will ask about the nature of the material in Genesis. The only honest answer is that they contain very old traditions which are not the unique possessions of Israel. This kind of literature belongs to the Ancient Near East. *The Babylonian Creation Epic* and *The Gilgamesh Epic* are the best-known examples and they emerged among the people of Mesopotamia. There are many clear and distinct references to these traditions within the Old Testament. The evidence compels one to conclude that behind the Scriptures and the literature of the Ancient Near East, there stands a common tradition. However, the great value of Van der Ziel's book is that it does not end on this note. Within the covenant community of Israel, something has happened to these traditions. They have become the medium of revelation. The nature religion of the *Babylonian* and *Gilgamesh Epic* is ultimately an immanental religion. It is the forces of nature which have been deified and man seeks to manipulate them in order to secure a better integration with nature. The God of the Scriptures is radically different. These old traditions have been transformed and have become the medium through which the Lord speaks His word of judgment and mercy. It is in this perspective that one is able to sense the importance of the doctrine of inspiration.

For some years it has been my privilege to teach these chapters of Genesis at a theological seminary. For this reason,

I have sought to remain familiar with current Biblical studies in this area. It is a pleasure for me to assure every reader of this volume that this work stands in the best tradition of both historical and current Biblical studies.

John V. Halverson
Professor of Old Testament
Luther Theological Seminary
St. Paul, Minnesota

PREFACE

This book had its beginning in a series of lectures given for Lutheran pastors at the University Lutheran Student Center of the University of Minnesota. The aim of this lecture series was to approach the problem of science and theology from the exegetical side and to confront the results of such an investigation with what is held to be true in science. It is then possible to draw conclusions about the relationship between science and theology.

A previous book by the author, "The Natural Sciences and the Christian Message," approached the problem of science and theology from the side of science. The main aim was there to tell what science says and does not say, and to demonstrate that science and theology are radically different. The present book complements this by approaching the same problem from the Biblical side. Since many of the past conflicts between science and theology centered around the problems of "beginnings" and "origins," the theological discussion was restricted to Gen. 1-12, and the scientific discussion was limited to these problems.

Earlier theological discussions of Gen. 1-12 were often closely connected with obsolete scientific ideas, and this hampered rather than promoted the understanding of the text. The modern approach to Old Testament exegesis, especially the exegetical work of the German Old Testament scholar Gerhard von Rad, overcomes this difficulty and makes it fruitful to discuss the relationship between the scientific and the theological points of view. The author is greatly indebted to von Rad's work and has heavily borrowed from it.

If the discussion were restricted to the question what the Genesis text *says*, this book should have been written by an

Old Testament scholar. But if one is interested in the *relationship* between the message of Genesis and modern science, the scientific and the theological points of view should be presented *together*. And that means either that the theologian must become familiar with scientific thinking or that the scientist must learn the theological point of view. For that reason it is not so peculiar that a scientist is writing this book.

The author is indebted to Pastor Harry N. Huxhold for improvements in the manuscript, to Dr. V. Elving Anderson for improvements in the parts dealing with biology, and to Dr. K. M. van Vliet for stimulating discussions about many problems raised here. Mrs. van der Ziel typed the manuscript.

A. VAN DER ZIEL

CONTENTS

CHAPTER ONE

Introduction

1. The reasons for this investigation.

Concerned Christians in the past have had, and many at present still have, considerable difficulty in accepting scientific discoveries and theories concerning the world and its origin. They have feared, and many still fear, that they would have to forfeit the integrity of Scripture if they would do so. This problem had its origin in the manner in which the Biblical message, in particular the message of Genesis, was tied to 17th-century science. To overcome the difficulty, one should allow Genesis to *speak for itself,* without making premature connections with science and without introducing preconceived notions derived from science. It will then be seen that most of these problems disappear.

For others the problem seems at first sight to be of a quite different nature. They hold the first chapters of Genesis to be an ancient *explanation and view* of the world around us, that was once useful and valid but that has now been superseded by a scientific explanation and world view. The error made here is that it is not sufficiently understood that Genesis gives in the first place a *religious, theological* message. It does not try

11

to *explain,* but it *teaches* and *preaches* God as creator. To find that out, one must listen carefully to what Genesis tries to convey.

To do so requires a sacrifice on our part. The sacrifice is not, as some people think, that one has to accept something that is untrue. The main problem is the *framework of thought* within which the message of Genesis is told. This framework is that of the ancient Middle East in general and of the Israelitic population of Palestine in particular. It is quite different from the framework of modern Western thought. The sacrifice that must be made, is that we must let this framework *stand,* for only in that manner can we understand what Genesis has to tell.

The aim of this book is to confront the Biblical message of Genesis with what is presently held to be true in science. We should listen first to what Genesis has to say and then ask what science has to offer. Many of the aspects of the problem "science and theology" show up in such a discussion and for that reason is seems worth-while to devote our attention to it.

2. Genesis and science. Complementarity.

Genesis and science both deal with the world around us. But they do so in quite a different manner. Genesis, as will be seen later, tries to *relate* the world around us *to God,* declares God to be its creator and our creator[1]. Science, on the other hand, tries to "explain" the world around us by *interrelating* phenomena that can be observed in this world[2-5].

Genesis and science both deal with the problem of beginning. Genesis looks at this problem from a *theological* point of view. At the beginning stands no one but the God of Israel, who chose Israel as his own and made himself known to them.

Science also looks at the beginning of the world around us, but it looks at it from a *scientific* point of view. The question is then not "Who is behind it?" but instead, "What happened?"

Do these two points of view match? Before that question can be answered, a few earlier questions must be answered first; otherwise, only confusion will result. They are: a. What *are* the two points of view that must be compared? b. Are there reasons to suppose that they should match? c. What does it mean if they do, and what does it mean if they do not?

The first question will be dealt with in the first two parts of this book. The answer to the second question depends on one's attitude. In a *monistic* frame of thought the two points of view *should* match. If they do not, then one of them must be discarded in favor of the other. Many people are hidden monists, and as a consequence some *outside* the church disregard the Biblical point of view and adopt the scientific one, whereas some *inside* the church disregard the scientific point of view and accept the Biblical one. As long as both groups keep to their position, no enlightenment is possible and no advances can be made.

But not only are these two extreme points of view barren, they also overlook the possibility that seemingly conflicting points of view may present *different ways* of looking at the world around us and *different approaches* to reality. But if that is the case, then these seemingly conflicting points of view should be left *standing side by side,* knowing that their combination gives a better picture of reality than each single point of view can give. This is known as the *complementary point of view*[4]. If this complementary point of view applies, then there is no reason to suppose that the two points of view should match. Accidental points of agreement are then of little significance and points of disagreement do not become burning issues.

The Biblical writers of Genesis wrote without any knowledge of modern science and it would be preposterous to hold them accountable for modern scientific views. They lived and thought within the framework of the ancient world view. They did not give the message *for the sake* of the framework, but they gave it *within* the framework of their own thought and of the thought of their times. The Christian Church is not interested in the framework as such, it is interested in *transmitting* the message which it holds binding for the present. Though it is not possible to *separate* the message from the framework, it is necessary to *distinguish* between the two. This is one of the efforts of Biblical theology.

This is quite different from the way science looks at things. It is not interested in a *message;* it is interested in interrelating facts and observations. It is interested in *what happens* as far as *present* events are concerned and in *what happened* as far as *past* events are concerned. Though the Bible is very much interested in past events, since it holds that God acts in history, it is not interested in the events for their *own* sake. It is interested in *incorporating* these events into the message.

But if the Biblical and the scientific point of view are so far apart, how then does the scientific point of view come into the theological picture at all? It does so for two reasons. In the first place, by the sheer contrast between the modern world picture and the ancient world view, it helps to distinguish between the message and the framework. In the second place, the Biblical message must be *transmitted.* And that means that it must be presented within the framework of the *modern* world picture. Science comes in because it has shaped and is still shaping this picture.

How does the Biblical point of view come into the life of the scientist? It does not come to make a *direct* contribution to science, for science is self-consistent. But scientists are also human beings, moved by the same deep questions that move all other people. These deep questions cannot be answered by science and, unless one wants to solve the problem by declaring those questions meaningless, one must look for answers elsewhere. The answer to these deep questions is given by the *Bible,* and as a consequence the Bible has a message for scientists and nonscientists alike. It is thus seen that the Biblical point of view and the scientific viewpoint indeed complement each other on both sides.

The first part of this book deals with what Genesis 1-12 has to say. The second part relates what science has to tell about the world around us. *After* one has listened to both sides it becomes possible to draw some conclusions.

REFERENCES:

[1] Karl Barth, *Kirchliche Dogmatik,* Evangelischer Verlag A. G. Zollikon/Zürich. (Several volumes have appeared in English translation.)

[2] Herbert Butterfield, Editor, *A Short History of Science,* Anchor Books, 1958.

[3] Stephan Toulmin, *A Philosophy of Science,* Hutchinson Univ. Library 1955.

[4] Aldert van der Ziel, *The Natural Sciences and the Christian Message,* T. S. Denison & Co., Inc., Minneapolis, 1960.

[5] A. N. Whitehead, *Science and the Modern World,* Mentor Books, New York, 1948.

CHAPTER TWO

Biblical Exegesis As Applied to Genesis

1. Biblical exegesis.

Biblical exegesis consists of three related parts:

a. The understanding of the text at hand.

b. Relating the content of the text to other parts of the Bible.

c. Expressing the content of the text within the framework of today.

For an understanding of the text at hand the theologian has several tools at his disposal:

1. *Linguistic tools.* A thorough knowledge of the Hebrew language is necessary for rendering the text into present-day English. This is the task of experts, who spend their lifetime in the study of the Hebrew text. Those who do not have this knowledge must rely on them.

2. *Archaeological tools.* Archaeology has shed an important light on the background of the Old Testament. It has clarified many details of the history of Israel. Important findings, such as the Ras Shamra texts, have helped in a better understanding of Biblical Hebrew[10]. It has given an insight into the political, religious and literary background against which the Old Testa-

16

ment is placed. The Biblical account of the flood, for example, is paralleled by Babylonian flood accounts and it is helpful to compare and to contrast the two narratives (Chapter 8). The prophets, especially in the poetic passages of their work, freely refer to mythologies of surrounding people. Knowledge of these mythologies can help in understanding those passages. This again is the work of experts.

3. *Literary tools.* For an understanding of the text it is necessary to know whether one has to do with an historical account, a poem, a novel, a parable, preaching or teaching. This distinction is greatly helped by recognizing the different literary traditions of the Old Testament[1-4].

It is commonly accepted, even by quite conservative Old Testament scholars, that the first six books of the Old Testament (the Hexateuch) are composed of large blocks of different literary traditions. Since these traditions have a different theological background, the interpretation of a particular Old Testament passage depends upon the literary tradition of which it forms a part. As a first step in the understanding of the text it is therefore important to establish to which literary tradition the text belongs.

Relating the content of the text to other parts of the Bible and giving a unified and systematic account of its content is the aim of systematic theology, also known as dogmatics. Expressing the content within the framework of today is also the task of dogmatics as far as its systematic side is concerned. Its practical side is accomplished in *preaching*[5].

The message of a particular part of the Old Testament should not be prematurely connected to other parts of the Bible. Before something is connected to something else, one must know *what* is connected to *what*. Otherwise one may be connecting the wrong things. On the other hand the one part of the Old Testament should not be kept isolated from the other parts of the Bible. Ultimately the connections must be made.

There is therefore an intricate interplay between the various parts of the Bible. In some cases a particular passage cannot be seen in its proper perspective, unless its connection with other parts of the Bible is clarified beforehand. In the creation accounts, for example, it is necessary to remember that "creation" is not the predominant concept of the Old Testament. What predominates is God's choice of Israel as His people and God's bringing of Israel out of Egypt and into the promised land. The commandments always point to this important fact. And the prophets measure Israel's actual performance against its high calling. The creation accounts must be seen in the light of this background. Creation thus becomes a "conclusion of faith."

Many parts of the Old Testament are quoted in the New Testament. Such quotations can help in learning what is appropriate application of the Old Testament text according to the New Testament tradition. They give examples how *we* could apply this text. This does not mean that the interpretation of the Old Testament text is thereby exhausted. Neither does it mean that the example should always be followed slavishly.

For example, the Apostle Paul relates the word of Gen. 2: "Therefore shall a man leave his father and his mother, and shall cleave unto his wife: and they shall be one flesh" to Christ and His church. But this should not hold back the question what this passage of Gen. 2 means in its own context. The text is not exhausted by Paul's interpretation.

The Apostle Paul spoke to an audience that was steeped

in typological and allegorical interpretations of the text. For that reason he used those interpretations freely to get a nontypological and nonallegorical message across. At present allegorical and typological interpretations are not very useful.

The first few chapters of the Bible should not be interpreted allegorically. One should hold to the text *at hand*. Asking the question: "What does the Word actually say" is much more fruitful than letting one's imagination run wild. That does not mean, of course, that an imaginative interpretation should not be preferred over an unimaginative one!

Neither should typological interpretations be attempted. With this it is meant that one should refrain, for example, from seeing the travel of Israel through the Red Sea as a type or foreshadowing of Christian baptism (by the old baptismal liturgy of the Dutch Reformed Church), from seeing Noah's ark as a type of the church (by many Church-fathers) or from seeing everywhere in the Old Testament "types" of foreshadowings of Christ. What is concluded may be true, profound and edifying, but it has little to do with what the text actually says.

It cannot be denied, of course, that we have the same freedom as the New Testament writers with respect to allegories and typologies. The question is, however, whether we should make use of this freedom. We should if it is useful; we should not if it is not useful. At present the latter is often the case.

Von Rad [6-8] has pioneered with a careful use of a very particular form of typology. He does so in order to make the connection of particular Old Testament texts with the New Testament. What was said about typologies in general should not be held against von Rad's approach.

2. The different literary traditions.

That different literary traditions exist, is clear even to the casual onlooker. Gen. 2 differs strongly from Gen. 1, even though both deal essentially with the same problem of creation. Gen. 4 and 5 give both lists of Adam's descendants but discuss them in quite a different manner. The story of the flood (Gen. 6-8) runs unevenly with many repetitions and with inconsistencies about the duration of the flood. The most sensible approach is to consider the text as a combination of two independent accounts (Chapter 8). The table of nations (Chapter 10) can be separated into two different accounts and so there are many other instances. The separation of these literary traditions is usually easily accomplished, once one has grasped their existence. The existence of the various literary traditions is therefore almost as elementary a fact as that the original text is in Hebrew.

The basis of this critical literary study was laid by the "higher criticism" of the nineteenth century. For that reason there is still considerable fear in some circles that critical literary scholarship will destroy the Biblical message instead of helping its understanding. It should be understood, however, that the present outlook is quite different from what it was in the nineteenth century. Much has been learned and many new points of view have been introduced. Some of these can greatly help in understanding the Biblical text and making it a "living Word." The fact that the methods of critical literary scholarship were sometimes misused in the past, gives no reason to overlook its intrinsic value as a tool.

The fear is not unfounded, however, that an indiscriminate splitting of the text into different "sources" will destroy the unity of the Old Testament and leave only the ruins of the text behind. In the early days of "higher criticism" this was exactly what happened. The splitting of the text into "sources" is not done indiscriminately, however. Most scholars at present either hold to the three-tradition or to the four-tradition theory.

In the three-tradition theory the first four books of the Bible are seen as a composition taken from three sources known as J, E and P. J stands for "Jahwist" because it uses the name "Jahweh" for God, E stands for "Elohist," since it uses the name "Elohim" for God, whereas P stands for the tradition of the Priests. J is the oldest and comes from the Southern Kingdom. E is younger, dates from around 700 B.C., and comes from the Northern Kingdom. P is considerably younger; it dates from around 500 B.C. Each tradition, however, makes use of much older material[1].

The four-tradition theory distinguishes E and P as before, but splits J into two parts, an older part L, standing for "lay tradition" and a younger part J. Eissfeldt[1] dates L from the days of David and Solomon and the younger part J from around 750 B.C. Von Rad[2] assumes that the *extended* J (that is L + J) dates from around 950 B.C. The reason for the splitting of the extended J text into L + younger J is done because the extended J-group is considered to be too inhomogeneous to ascribe it to a single author.

Both theories hold that these literary traditions were quite early joined together in various editorial processes. First L was joined to J and then L + J was joined to E. Still later, P was joined to L + J + E to give the present first four books of the Old Testament[3].

The book of Deuteronomy and parts of the book of Joshua belong to the Deuteronomic school; this tradition is designated as D. It is connected with the attempted reformation of the cult, associated with the discovery of a "Book of Law" in the Temple under King Josiah (II Kings 22) in 621 B.C. The Hexateuch thus consists of contributions from L, J, E, P and D.

Gen. 1-12 is a composition of J and P if one adheres to the three-tradition theory and of L, J and P if one follows the four-tradition theory. The E-tradition, at least in its present form, starts with Abraham (Gen. 20:1-18).

The distinction of these traditions is important for the interpretation of the text. For example, P is rather prosaic, means everything exactly as it is said and does not use figurative language. J gives a much more artistic, imaginative account, full of symbolism and hidden meanings, so that one has to know how to read between the lines.

Modern critical scholarship, therefore, does not hold the first five books of the Old Testament to be written by Moses. But the various literary traditions were each meant as a unity and the editorially joining together of the various traditions emphasizes the essential unity of the *total text*. Hence, despite the fact that the unity is not established by a single authorship, it is by no means less impressive.

This means that the various literary traditions should not be played one against the other. That would violate the *whole* structure of the Old Testament. They should be seen as a unity, and should be used to *complement* each other. If that is done, the study of the various literary traditions can become a useful tool in the understanding of the text.

It is held in some circles that the splitting of the text into its literary components denies that the Bible is God's Word. There is, of course, the danger that the Bible is viewed as mere literature. But God's Word comes to us as *human words*. In order to understand these words as God's words, what they really are, their human character must be taken seriously. And that means that the study of the various literary traditions, which emphasizes this human character of the words, is both useful and necessary.

3. Genesis and history.

Gen. 1-12 is often labeled as "prehistory," or in German "Urgeschichte." This rightly emphasizes the fact that this part of Genesis deals with events that are less easily historically verifiable than some events dealt with in later sections of the Bible. But it could give the erroneous impression that these chapters of Genesis do not deal with actual events at all but teach universal and general truths.

When is an event to be called historical? When it can be verified by the tools that modern history has at its disposal. The longer ago the event has occurred, the most difficult it will usually be to verify its occurrence. It should, therefore, not come as a great shock if some of the events dealt with in the Bible cannot be verified historically. That does not rob it necessarily of its character of an actual event.

The Bible was not written as a science book, but neither was it written as a history book. The Bible is "history" in the broader sense that "God has a history with man." It is God's history of man's salvation ("Heilsgeschichte" in German). It is important that the history that God has with man is actually believed. For our faith stands or falls with it. But this kind of history is not found in history books. We find it only in the Bible.

Some parts of the Old Testament are historically more or less verifiable. A considerable part of the stories around King

David, for example, seem to have been taken directly from the royal archives and can thus be classified eminently as historical writings[7]. This is more the exception than the rule, however.

The reason for this is not that the Bible is uninterested in history. It *is* interested in history, for it holds that God *acts* in history. But just because the Bible is interested in *God's acts in history,* it must follow that it is not interested in the events *for their own sake. The events lead to the message,* and it is the *message* that is of primary importance. For that reason one should not be surprised that essential parts of the Biblical text are historically nonverifiable.

Let this be illustrated by the following example. In the book of Kings we often read: "King X was . . . years old when he became king and he reigned . . . years in Jerusalem. And he did what was evil in the sight of the Lord." The first statement can be verified by historical means, but the second cannot, since the historian has no tools at his disposal to decide whether or not King X did indeed "what was evil in the sight of the Lord." The latter is thus an "unhistorical" verdict, even though it may well have been quite justified.

In other cases the connection to history is much more remote. For example, in the case of the creation accounts (Gen. 1 and Gen. 2) the historical "facts" are completely in the background and the "message" reigns supreme. In other cases, e.g. in the flood accounts, the story refers to a real event, but it does so in order to bring the message of sin and grace across. Nowhere is history dealt with for its *own* sake; it is always for the sake of a particular *message.*

Even where this is done, the text never tries to present "universal and general truths" but proclaims very particular truths. For example, in Gen. 1 and 2 it is taught or proclaimed that the God of Israel is the creator of heaven and earth[7]. In Gen. 3 it is proclaimed: "You are a sinner and your God punishes and forgives sins." Gen 6-8 proclaims the message of sin and grace. And so one could go on.

Should the stories of Gen. 1-12 be called "myths"? That depends on how the word myth is defined. According to Webster's dictionary a myth is "a story, the origin of which is forgotten, ostensibly historical, but usually such as to explain some practice, belief, institution, or natural phenomenon." That does not fit too well with what Gen. 1-12 tries to do. It preaches and teaches that God is creator, and that God has a history with man, a history of human sin and divine grace.

That does not deny that the Bible may use mythological concepts borrowed from Israel's environment. But it uses them to get a *message* across. For example, Gen. 1 speaks of the "Tannim of the sea," which are mythological sea monsters. But it introduces them to state explicitly that they are under God's control. Gen. 2 speaks of a man made of clay and of a woman made of man's rib. But as shown in Chapter 4, these concepts are introduced for aetiological, rather than mythological purposes. Gen. 6 speaks of marriages between heavenly beings and the daughters of man. But this is not done to *explain* the existence of heroes and men of fame, but rather to *proclaim* once more that man is a sinner. And so we could go on.

German theologians like to use the German word "Sage" when dealing with Gen. 1-12. This word, that has no adequate English equivalent, is probably safer to use than the word "myth."* When applied to a nation, "Sage" is the form in

---

*According to Webster's dictionary a "legend" is "Any story coming down from the past, especially one popularly taken as historical though not verifiable." A "Sage" is much more than that, and hence the word "Sage" should not be translated as "legend."

which the nation conceives its history (von Rad[2]). It conveys real insight into this history. It is not the product of poetic fantasy, but should be taken seriously. It wants to be believed. So, Gen. 1-12 conveys real insight into the history that God has with man.

REFERENCES:

[1] Otto Eissfeldt, *Die Genesis der Genesis*, J. C. B. Mohr, Tübingen, 1958. Also appeared in Interpreters Dictionary of the Bible, Abingdon Press, New York.

[2] Gerhard von Rad, *Das Alte Testament Deutsch*, Vol. 2, Das erste Buch Mose, Kap. 1-12/9, Verlag Van den Hoeck and Ruprecht, Göttingen, 1949.

[3] Alan Richardson, Genesis I-XI, *The Torch Bible Commentaries*, SCM Press Ltd., London, 1953.

[4] Hellmuth Frey, *Das Buch der Anfänge*, Kapitel 1-11 des ersten Buches Mose, Calwer Verlag, Stuttgart, 1958.

[5] Helmut Thielicke, *Wie die Welt began*, Quell Verlag, Stuttgart, 1960. (A series of sermons on Gen. 1-9.)

[6] Gerhard von Rad, *Theologie des Alten Testaments*, Band I, Chr. Kaiser Verlag, München, 1961.

[7] Gerhard von Rad, *Gesammelte Studien zum Alten Testament*, Chr. Kaiser Verlag, München, 1958.

[8] Claus Westermann, Editor, *Probleme alttestamentlicher Hermeneutik*, Chr. Kaiser Verlag, München, 1960.

[9] Walther Zimmerli, *Das Alte Testament als Anrede*, Chr. Kaiser Verlag, München, 1956.

[10] D. Winton Thomas, Editor, *Documents from Old Testament Times*, Thomas Nelson and Sons Ltd., London, 1962.

CHAPTER THREE

The Teaching of God As Creator

1. The Text. Gen. 1:1-2:4a (P).

(1) In the beginning God created the heaven and the earth. (2) And the earth was without form, and void; and darkness was upon the face of the deep. And the Spirit of God moved upon the face of the waters. (3) And God said, Let there be light: and there was light. (4) And God saw the light, that it was good: and God divided the light from the darkness. (5) And God called the light Day, and the darkness he called Night. And the evening and the morning were the first day.

(6) And God said, Let there be a firmament in the midst of the waters, and let it divide the waters from the waters. (7) And God made the firmament, and divided the waters which were under the firmament from the waters which were above the firmament: and it was so. (8) And God called the firmament Heaven. And the evening and the morning were the second day.

(9) And God said, Let the waters under the heaven be gathered together unto one place, and let the dry land appear: and it was so. (10) And God called the dry land Earth; and the gathering together of the waters called he Seas: and God saw that it was good. (11) And God said, Let the earth bring forth

grass, the herb yielding seed, and the fruit tree yielding fruit after his kind, whose seed is in itself, upon the earth: and it was so. (12) And the earth brought forth grass, and herb yielding seed after his kind, and the tree yielding fruit, whose seed was in itself, after his kind: and God saw that it was good. (13) And the evening and the morning were the third day.

(14) And God said, Let there be lights in the firmament of the heaven to divide the day from the night; and let them be for signs, and for seasons, and for days, and years: (15) And let them be for lights in the firmament of the heaven to give light upon the earth: and it was so. (16) And God made two great lights; the greater light to rule the day, and the lesser light to rule the night: he made the stars also. (17) And God set them in the firmament of the heaven to give light upon the earth, (18) And to rule over the day and over the night, and to divide the light from the darkness: and God saw that it was good. (19) And the evening and the morning were the fourth day.

(20) And God said, Let the waters bring forth abundantly the moving creature that hath life, and fowl that may fly above the earth in the open firmament of heaven. (21) And God created great whales, and every living creature that moveth, which the waters brought forth abundantly, after their kind, and every winged fowl after his kind: and God saw that it was good. (22) And God blessed them, saying, Be fruitful, and multiply, and fill the waters in the seas, and let fowl multiply in the earth. (23) And the evening and the morning were the fifth day.

(24) And God said, Let the earth bring forth the living creature after his kind, cattle, and creeping thing, and beast of the earth after his kind: and it was so. (25) And God made the

beast of the earth after his kind, and cattle after their kind, and every thing that creepeth upon the earth after his kind: and God saw that it was good.

(26) And God said, Let us make man in our image, after our likeness: and let them have dominion over the fish of the sea, and over the fowl of the air, and over the cattle, and over all the earth, and over every creeping thing that creepeth upon the earth. (27) So God created man in his own image, in the image of God created he him; male and female created he them. (28) And God blessed them, and God said unto them, Be fruitful, and multiply, and replenish the earth, and subdue it: and have dominion over the fish of the sea, and over the fowl of the air, and over every living thing that moveth upon the earth.

(29) And God said, Behold, I have given you every herb bearing seed, which is upon the face of all the earth, and every tree, in which is the fruit of a tree yielding seed; to you it shall be for meat. (30) And to every beast of the earth, and to every fowl of the air, and to every thing that creepeth upon the earth, wherein there is life, I have given every green herb for meat: and it was so. (31) And God saw every thing that he had made, and, behold, it was very good. And the evening and the morning were the sixth day.

(2:1) Thus the heavens and the earth were finished, and all the host of them. (2:2) And on the seventh day God ended his work which he had made; and he rested on the seventh day from all his work which he had made. (2:3) And God blessed the seventh day, and sanctified it: because that in it he had rested from all his work which God created and made. (2:4a) These are the generations of the heavens and of the earth when they were created.

2. Discussion of the text.

Neither in J nor in P does the "doctrine of creation" as such form a central part of the faith. Both literary traditions stand in principle in the faith of salvation and election. The Ten Commandments are prefaced by the phrase: "I am the Lord thy God, which have brought thee out of the land of Egypt, out of the house of bondage" (Ex. 20:2), not by: "I am the Lord thy God, which created thee." Both J and P proclaim, however, that this Jahweh, who made first His covenant with Abraham and elected him, and who later made His covenant with Israel and elected it, is *also* the creator of the world. *Creation is a conclusion of faith.*

To understand what it means that Gen. 1 belongs to P, we quote Gerhard von Rad[1]. "This Chapter is teaching of the priests; it contains the essence of priestly knowledge in its most concentrated form. It was not 'written' one day, but it is doctrine that enriched itself carefully in a very slow growth process stretching out over hundreds of years. Here is nothing arbitrary; everything is well thought through, well-balanced, and should be taken precisely as said. It is therefore wrong here—even if it is done only at certain points—to reckon with archaic and half-mythological rudiments that one can consider as deserving reverence but that are not considered binding theologically and conceptually. What is said here holds as it is put down, completely and exactly. Moreover, nowhere is it speaking in a symbolic or even poetic fashion."*

The P-account has a beginning and it has an end. The beginning is: "In the beginning God created the heaven and the earth" and the end is: "These are the generations of the heavens

---

*Page 36 of von Rad's book.

and of the earth when they were created." The first is the title or summary of what follows and the latter is the conclusion.[8] The P-account of creation formed part of a "book of generations," in which Gen. 5, starting with: "This is the book of the generations of Adam" was preceded by Gen. 1:1-2:4a. To make the connection, the account of creation ends by speaking about "the generations of the heavens and of the earth."

An earlier school of theologians suggested that Gen. 1:1 pictured the supreme event of "creation out of nothing" and that the remaining part of Gen. 1 tells how the earth, first created "without form and void" was modified to become habitable. This seems a strange interpretation, however. For every remaining act of creation is prefaced by the phrase: "And God said . . ." and usually followed by "And God made . . ." or by "And God created . . ." Hence, such a "supreme event" would certainly have been prefaced in that manner. That this is not done speaks against the older interpretation. Moreover, the concept of a "creation out of nothing" is far too abstract to be used here; it belongs to a much later time.

Others have proposed that verse 2 should be read as: "The earth became without form and void," suggesting a kind of a "fall." The remainder should then tell about the "restoration" of the earth. The text does not give any support to such a suggestion.

The word used for God is *Elohim.* Though its form is plural, it should not be considered as a remnant of earlier polytheism. It means that God, though one, is not a lonely God. There is a plural in God, that comes to the foreground in solemn decisions such as "Let us make man . . ." (Gen. 1:26a), "Behold, the man has become as one of us . . ." (Gen. 3:22a), "Go to, let us go down, and there confound their language . . ."

(Gen. 11:7a), found both in P and J. It is not, however, a full development of the doctrine of Trinity as some Christian Fathers thought. Alan Richardson[2] puts it as follows: "Of course, the O. T. writers had no such conception in mind; but yet they were in their own way insisting upon that truth which the doctrine of the Trinity teaches—that a 'unitarian' or lonely God is not the God of historic biblical revelation."*

The word "bara" means "to create." Israel used it only when speaking about God's creative activity and never in connection with man's creative activity. Moreover, it is never connected with any indication of material used in the creative process. For that reason it is often thought (for example, by Gerhard von Rad[1] and by Karl Barth[5]) that it contains the idea of a "creation out of nothing." It is doubtful, however, whether that idea was in the mind of the author of Gen. 1[7]. We come back to this problem later.

"Heaven and earth" means "all of creation" or "the whole universe." With the one sentence of Gen. 1:1 God is thus proclaimed as the creator of *all*.

If Gen. 1:1 is the summary of the creation account, then the account itself starts with verse 2. It is a most peculiar beginning. Does it mean that the first act of creation is the creation of the "chaos" of which Gen. 1:2 speaks? This is hardly the case, for apparently the first act of creation is the creation of light. It seems to indicate one thing: The great work of creation has not yet started, but it is about to begin. The earth is still void and without form and darkness is still upon the face of the deep. The work of creation aims at overcoming the "chaos" of Gen. 1:2; it declares this chaos to be obsolete and done away with[5].

---

*Page 46 of Richardson's book.

To accentuate the chaos, the text states that "a strong wind*
moved upon the face of the waters." Some theologians interpret
this passage as God hovering or brooding like a mother bird
over the newborn world[3]. It is very unlikely that this is the
meaning of the original.

In the ancient Middle East, and even up to relatively recent
times, all work was done during daytime, and night was the
time when nobody could work. For that reason the first act of
creation is the creation of light. But much more than light
appears here: the rhythm of day and night is established. The
author does not tell *how* the rhythm of day and night was established; he merely states that it *was*. Since the creation of the
sun, moon and stars occurred on the fourth day and since their
rule over day and night was established on that day, it is obvious that the author did not consider them as having performed
that function before. The meaning of this particular twist in
the account will be discussed later.

"And God divided (separated) the light from the darkness." Creation means "separation," both here and in the next
few verses. Later it means "bringing into being."

"And God called the light Day, and the darkness he called
Night." The essence of the day and the night is hereby established and God is proclaimed as the ruler over the day and
over the night. The last is especially important, for to the
primitive mind the chaos seems to regain a certain power over
creation during darkness. It is therefore important to know
that it is only a limited power; God rules over it.

"And God saw the light, that it was good." That is, the

---

*The word "ruach" means spirit, breath or wind, but in this context it more
likely refers to the latter. The expression "wind of God" should be interpreted
as a superlative, hence "a strong wind."

light served the purpose that God meant it to serve: to establish the rhythm of day and night. The expression "And God
saw . . ." occurs every time a certain work of creation has been
completed.

Besides giving an arrangement of the various acts of creation in a very distinct order, the P account of creation also has
a seven-day week superimposed upon it. For that reason it is
added: "And the evening and the morning were the first day."
The meaning of this superposition will be discussed later.

Now that this has been accomplished, the great work of
creation can continue. Conversely, one can say that if this is
the *real* beginning of creation, then Gen. 1:1 does not refer
to a creation of a formless earth out of nothing. This will be
fortified by the account of the next few acts of creation.

In the account of the second day of creation ancient concepts are used in great abundance and their use has a particular
significance for us, as will be seen shortly. It starts as follows:
"And God said, Let there be a firmament in the midst of the
waters, and let it divide (separate) the waters from the waters."
What is meant here is that the arch of the sky is erected as a
solid hemisphere, separating the waters above the firmament
(stored in heaven) from the waters below it.

It is often suggested that the word "firmament" should be
interpreted as "atmosphere." This is incorrect, for the corresponding word in the original means "expanse," it is something
that is rolled out or stretched out as a tent. It is something
solid and not something gaseous. Moreover, our modern concept of "atmosphere" would be alien to ancient Eastern
thought.

In ancient thought, water was thought to be stored in heaven and dispensed on earth as rain through windows in the sky. Heaven was also considered as having storage space for snow and hail, as the book of Job mentions. To speak of "water stored in heaven" is thus in complete accord with ancient understanding.

To let this understanding *stand,* without replacing it by modern concepts, is important. For through it the story proclaims explicitly that the world as the ancient Middle East *saw* it is God's creation. The message of God's creative acts comes to us *through* this ancient framework; in it the faith in God as creator of heaven and earth is expressed. This means that *we* should express the message of God's creative acts, and *our* faith in God as creator, within the framework of *modern* ideas. That is not done to make the message of Genesis obsolete; it is done to make it *fruitful.* The creation account of Genesis thereby remains our guide, to ensure that the message that is relayed is actually the *Biblical* message and not the product of our own imagination. Correctly speaking about God as creator means *applying* Gen. 1.

"And God called the firmament Heaven." The firmament is thereby characterized in its properties and God's rule is proclaimed over it. What goes on in heaven is under God's power and domain.

"And the evening and the morning were the second day." Note that it is not said "And God saw that it was good" as follows after each creative act. Such a statement comes only after the dry land and the seas have been separated. Apparently the creation of Heaven, Earth and the Seas are considered together as a single act. This act spreads over more than one day, however, indicating once again that the seven-day week is *superimposed* upon the various acts of creation.

"And God said, Let the waters under the heaven be gathered together unto one place, and let the dry land appear: and it was so." The earth, the seas and the heaven have thereby been created.

"And God called the dry land Earth; and the gathering of the waters called he Seas." The earth and the seas are thereby characterized in their properties and God's rule is established over them. What occurs on earth is under God's power and domain. The seas, though seemingly a manifestation of the original chaos, are actually under God's control and should therefore not be feared. Moreover, the sea is not divine, as some ancient mythologies thought; it is a fellow creature, created by God and part of His domain.

There is now space for the plants and the trees to grow, for the animals and man to walk, for the birds to fly and for the fish to swim. The earth is ready for habitation and the heaven is ready for the sun, moon and stars to take their course. For that reason the story concludes: "And God saw that it was good." This indicates that the creation of heaven, earth and seas forms a *single* work of creation. Moreover, all serve the purpose that they were meant to serve.

Before continuing let us look back for a moment. We saw that "creation" meant "separation"; light is separated from darkness, the firmament separates the waters above the firmament from those below it and the earth is separated from the seas. This seems to go against the idea of a "creation out of nothing."

Objections to the idea of "creation out of nothing" would disappear if this "nothing" were identified with "the earth without form and void, with darkness upon the face of the deep, and with a strong wind moving upon the face of the waters."

The "nothing" is then a concrete concept familiar to ancient thought and not an abstract concept alien to ancient thought.

This does not mean that the concept of "creation out of nothing" cannot be useful. As a matter of fact, it is quite useful in that it stresses God's freedom. When heaven and earth were created, God acted in freedom, not out of necessity. The text, however, stresses God's freedom without using this concept.

Since the Genesis account often uses the phrase: "And God said . . ." the concept of "creation by the Word," or *"fiat* creation" has been introduced. It is often said that this indicates the great "ease" with which God performed His creative acts. Such a statement tends to underestimate the tremendous powers that God has at His disposal. Only His word is needed to bring them into play, just as a great army commander only has to give his commands and the whole army is set into motion. From "fiat creation" it is only a relatively small step to consider the acts of creation as a kind of magic. But such magical aspects are completely alien to the text. God is creator, He is not a magician.

"And God said . . ." means that God expressed Himself. Creation is therefore not so much a command or a physical act. Rather it is an act of God's self-expression.

The first part of the creation account has now been given, and the second part begins. First the grass, the seed-yielding herb and the fruit-yielding trees are created on the third day, to prepare food for the animals and man that are about to appear.

The story begins: "And God said, Let the earth bring forth . . ." and continues with: "And the earth brought forth . . ." The creative act, that is the command to bring forth, and the natural response, that is the bringing forth, go hand in hand. There is no discrepancy between "creation" and "natural order" or "natural processes" in the account. Apparently the teller of the story and his readers and listeners found it quite natural that the *earth* should bring forth the grass, the herbs and the trees. To construct a discrepancy between "creation" and "natural process" is a modern fallacy to which one should not fall victim.

The account speaks of the grass, the seed and the trees that they were created "after their kind." Some early biologists have suggested that the word "kind" should be interpreted as "species" or "genus." Every species, or at least every genus, was seen as a "special creation" of God and these species were immutable. Moreover, "creation" was meant as a special *biological* act of the Creator. It is understandable that the originators of systematic biology thus tried to read their species concept "into" the text. The text, however, does not say anything like it. The word "kind" is used in a colloquial sense, not in a scientific sense, and the act of creation consists in that the earth brings forth.

The sun, moon and stars are created on the fourth day. In this part of the creation account special emphasis is placed on God's creative activity. This is done by stating "And God said . . . ," followed by: "And God created . . ." and ending by: "And God set them in the firmament . . ." If one wants to use the idea of "special creation" at all, here is a place where it would be appropriate to do so.

The emphasis is made for a very special reason. In the ancient Middle East the sun, moon and stars were worshipped as deities. To counteract this, the story emphasizes that the sun, moon and stars are *creatures*. True enough, they have the power to give light and to rule over the day and over the night, but it is *derived* power. God gave it to them.

The Semitic words for "sun" and "moon" were also names of gods. But for Israel they are *not* gods, they are creatures. For that reason their proper names should not even be *mentioned* in the creation account. They are described by the much more neutral words "the greater light" and "the lesser light" and thereby they are further degraded. This is part of Israel's "demythologization" of the world around it.

The rule of the sun, moon and stars is not a *divine* rule, but it is actually a service. They are not gods, they are *servants,* playing part in the "liturgy" of all creation. They serve "for signs, for seasons, and for days, and years." To emphasize this even stronger and to carry the demythologization even farther, the story tells that the rhythm of day and night was established earlier, on the first day. Only on the fourth day was this rhythm "hooked onto" the sun, moon and stars. This emphasizes that God did not give them their power out of necessity, but He did so in His freedom. He could have done otherwise and, as the story tells it, He actually did so by creating the light *first.* The sun, moon and stars are thereby robbed of their glory and become creatures, servants of God.

The achievement of the fourth day is summed up in the statement "And God saw that it was good." That is the sun, moon and stars served the purpose that God meant them to serve; they performed their duties perfectly.

On the fifth day the fishes and the birds are created. Here the King James version has the statements: "Let the waters bring forth abundantly the moving creature . . ." and "every living creature that moveth, which the waters brought forth abundantly . . ." Modern translators, like von Rad[1], read here:

"Let the waters abound with an abundance of living creatures . . ." and: ". . . all living creatures of which the waters
abounded . . ."* If the King James version is adhered to one
could again say that the creative act (the command to bring
forth) and the natural response (the bringing forth) go together and should not be seen as contrasts. Since the other
interpretation is possible, however, it is better to be careful and
not to read this conclusion into the text.

"And God created great whales . . ." The "whales" of
the King James version are actually mythological sea monsters:
"the Tannim of the sea." The text states specifically that *they*
too were *created*. The power that they have is the power that
God gave to them. They are fellow creatures for which one does
not have to be afraid.

The text emphasizes God's creative activity more than in
the case of the creation of the grass, the herbs and the trees.
It starts with: "And God said . . ." and continues with: "And
God created . . ." Apparently the fish and the fowl are closer
to God than the plants and the trees and hence God's creative
activity is emphasized more.

The fishes and the fowl are given the blessing: "Be fruitful, and multiply . . . ," thus indicating that animal reproduction
is part of God's good creation.

The sea is now populated with living creatures from fishes
to sea monsters and birds populate the space between the firmament and the earth. The purpose of the fifth day is thereby fully
accomplished and hence the story concludes: "And God saw
that it was good."

The first part of the sixth day brings the creation of the

*G. von Rad, page 35.

land animals. Again we read: "And God said . . . ," and: "And God made . . ." together with "Let the earth bring forth . . ." As before, the command to bring forth and the earth's response are not seen as contrasts, but they are seen together; they go hand in hand. The earth again does not bring forth by itself, it only does so upon God's command. This emphasizes that God has power over nature and that nature obeys God's command.

Again, there is no reference to "special creation" of the individual species or to the immutability of species. These are things that the 17th and 18th century *read into* the text, but it is not supported by the text as such.

The creation of all the land animals is seen as an act of creation separate from the creation of man. For that reason the story concludes here: "And God saw that it was good."

The work of the sixth day is not completed, however, for man is still missing from the scene. The creation of man is accomplished during the second half of the sixth day. The scheme of the seven-day week of creation once again does not coincide with the individual acts of creation. Sometimes a single act of creation is spread over two days and sometimes more than one act of creation is accomplished in a single day. This indicates once again that the seven-day week is *superimposed* upon the creation account. The reason for this superposition will be dealt with shortly.

The language suddenly becomes more solemn: "And God said, let us make man in our image, after our likeness . . . So, God created man in his own image, in the image of God created he him; male and female created he them." Apparently the story reaches a climax here. The original emphasizes this by using the verb "bara" for creation as in Gen. 1:1. Man's creation is thus singled out and receives a special emphasis that points to man's task and position. If one wants to use the concept of "special creation," here is another place to do so.

The word "us" is not used in the sense of a "pluralis majestatis"; about this the interpreters agree. Again, the word "us" indicates that God, though one, is not alone. Though this points in the direction of the Trinity, it does not do so explicitly and for that reason it is wise not to read too much into the passage. Otherwise, however, the opinion about the passage is divided. Some Old Testament scholars hold that God addresses His heavenly court surrounding Him, whereas others think that God addresses Himself.

Even more difference of opinion exists about the expression: "image of God."[1-5] Some theologians hold that this refers to man's state of innocence and righteousness before the fall and that this "image of God" was lost after the fall. Most Old Testament scholars deny that this is the case, since the expression is used after the fall (Gen. 5:1, 3; Gen. 9:6).

What then does this expression mean? It singles out man from the whole creation, not for a particular honor, but for a particular *service*. He rules over the animals and the earth and as such he is God's representative. This has not been obliterated by the fall, though some of its aspects have changed. If, for example, we look at what man has achieved in mastering the earth and unlocking the secrets of nature, then one sees that the promise of creation still holds. If we see, however, how this mastery over the earth and over nature can be misused, we realize that man's sin casts a deep shadow over this achievement.

The expression also indicates a close relationship between God and man. Just as man's creation as male and female establishes the marriage relationship, so man's creation in the image of God establishes the relationship between God and man[5]. Of all creation man alone is conscious of his responsibility before God. Man alone is aware that he stands in God's presence and under God's judgment. This relationship has been *changed* by the fall, but it was not *lost*[2].

Man thus receives from God his work "to subdue the earth and to have dominion over it and over all life on it." This means that man's work is seen as part of God's good creation. This aspect of man's work was not lost by the fall, even though Gen. 3 knows of another, darker aspect of our work.

Man receives from God his marriage relationship. The differentiation of the sexes and the relationship between the sexes is seen as part of God's good creation. So is the blessing of fruitfulness and procreation. These intents on God's part were not lost by the fall, even though Gen. 3 knows of another, darker aspect of the relationship between the sexes.

Man and beast receive their food from God. It should be noted that this food is strictly vegetarian. In the Bible this pictures a creation not soiled by human sin. As such it appears at the beginning (Gen. 1) when heaven and earth are created and toward the end (Isaiah 11) when a new heaven and a new earth appear.

This vegetarian food is a *theological* notion and *not* a biological one. It would therefore be wrong to conclude, as is sometimes done, that carnivorous animals eat other animals because of man's fall into sin. The statements about man's food and about man's fall should not be combined into an *explanation* of the present conditions found in the animal kingdom; they are *theological* statements.

The work of creation is now completed. That the work of

creation is seen as completed follows from the statement: "Thus the heavens and the earth were finished, and all the host of them." What God set out to accomplish has been accomplished and all serves the purpose that God meant it to serve. For that reason the author concludes: "And God saw everything that he had made, and, behold, it was very good."

But the story is not finished yet. What is missing is the *purpose* of creation. One purpose was, of course, that the earth should be populated by all kinds of living creatures and of man. But there was another purpose, for the story continues: "And on the seventh day God ended his work which he had made; and he rested on the seventh day from all his work which he had made. And God blessed the seventh day, and sanctified it: because that in it he had rested from all his work which God created and made."

The purpose of creation is stated in this allusion to the Sabbath day, which is sanctified, that is, "set apart" from the other days[5]. The seventh day or the Sabbath day in the Old Testament is a day of *praise* and *rejoicing*. Who should be praised? Who but the God who saved His people out of Egypt and made them His own! His name deserves praise and glory and His great works deserve to be praised. The purpose of creation in general and man's creation in particular is therefore that God should be glorified and that His name should be praised. Man is singled out for this task.

This is also the reason for the seven-day week of creation. It is superimposed upon the creation account to let it culminate in this message. It is not introduced to indicate the *duration* of creation. For that reason it makes little sense to extend the six days of creative activity into six periods of indefinite length.

Such a procedure obscures the creation account and ignores the importance of the seventh day.

The story says that God "rested on the seventh day from all his work which God created and made." Resting does not mean "doing nothing." When it is stated that God "rested" from His creative work, then this does not imply that His love, care and grace toward man ever rest.

The story of creation has now been told. The God of Israel has been proclaimed as creator of heaven and earth, of all living creatures and man. They are all seen as part of God's great plan, appearing at His command and by His decision. *That* is creation. This Biblical view does not exclude natural causes but encompasses them.

The teaching of Luther's small catechism: "I believe that God has created me and all creatures . . ." agrees with this. It, too, directly relates our existence to God. It, too, does not deny any of the processes that were needed to bring us into the world but encompasses them. He who reads Gen. 1 and concludes: "I believe that God has created me . . ." has understood its meaning perfectly.

"Creation" does not mean "sudden appearance," but its content is much richer than that. Neither is God our creator because in the dim past He turned the switch that set the universe into motion. That is 17th-century deism. That God is our creator means that by *using* all the processes that were needed to bring us into the world, *He* gave us our existence. This existence has *meaning,* because *God* gave it to us.

That this is the case can also be concluded from the end of the creation account: "These are the generations of the heavens and of the earth when they were created." We saw before that this statement connects Gen. 1 with Gen. 5. But it does more than that, for the word "generations" can be interpreted as "births." In the ancient Middle East the beginning of heaven and earth was often pictured as a birth and so the end of the P-account of creation can be seen as a polemic against it. But it should be understood that "creation" and "birth" are not seen as absolute contrasts. On the contrary, the statement might be read as: "The births of the heavens and the earth was that they were created."[6]

This can again be seen as an indication that the modern concept of "natural development" and the Biblical concept of "creation" are not absolute contrasts either. The "births" of which Israel's environment spoke compare with the modern concept of natural development. One might thus say: "The natural development of the heavens and the earth was that they were created." God operates through natural processes and the Biblical view of creation takes these processes into account.

The story of creation as given by P is sometimes called a "myth." This is confusing. A myth* is "a story, the origin of which is forgotten, ostensibly historical but usually such as to explain some practice, belief, institution or natural phenomenon." This does not fit very well what P tries to do. For not only is P's account of creation a continuous polemic against ancient mythologies, but even the words that are used have been carefully cleansed of their mythological content. Gen. 1 does not "explain," but it relates the world around us to God. That is not what a myth tries to do.

The story of creation given by P is sometimes called a "parable." A parable** is "a short fictitious narrative from

---

*Webster's New Collegiate Dictionary.
**Webster l. c.

which a moral or spiritual truth is drawn." That is not what Gen. 1 tries to do either. It does not try to relay moral or spiritual truths but bluntly states that the God of Israel is the creator of all and that all the world is His domain.

The story of creation as given by P is a very systematic account. For that reason it is not so surprising that many attempts have been made to compare the P-version with what modern science has to say. For science also gives a very systematic account of the world around us. It should not be forgotten, however, that the two systematic endeavors have a different aim. Gen. 1 systematically relates everything to God and declares it to be God's creation. Modern science systematically interrelates the observations of the world around us with the aim of giving a unified comprehensive description of it. That is not the same.

It is often helpful to make a distinction between the "framework" and the "message." It is difficult to *separate* the message from the framework and those who have tried to do so have often ended up in eliminating vital parts of the message. Every part of P's account, be it ever so much colored by the framework, aims in fact at telling the message of the God of Israel as creator of heaven and earth. For that reason we should let the story *stand as it is,* listen to its message and then apply it to our situation.

We interpreted Gen. 1:1 as the title of the creation account. Some modern translations suggest a different interpretation. For example *The Anchor Bible* (Doubleday and Co.) gives:

When God set about to create heaven and earth—the world being then a formless waste, with darkness over the seas and only an awesome wind sweeping over the water—God said "Let there be light." And there was light.

This translation thus sees the first act of creation as the creation of light. Gen. 1:1 is therefore not seen as the supreme event of a creation out of nothing. Nor does the translation suggest the idea that the chaos was created.

REFERENCES:

1Gerhard von Rad, *Das Alte Testament Deutsch*, Vol. 2, Das erste Buch Mose, Kap. 1-12/9, Verlag Van den Hoeck and Ruprecht, Göttingen, 1949.

2Alan Richardson, Genesis I-XI, *The Torch Bible Commentaries*, SCM Press Ltd., London, 1953.

3Hellmuth Frey, *Das Buch der Anfänge*, Kapitel 1-11 des ersten Buches Mose, Calwer Verlag, Stuttgart, 1958.

4Dietrich Bonhoeffer, *Schöpfung und Fall*, Chr. Kaiser Verlag, München, 1958.

5Karl Barth, *Kirchliche Dogmatik*, Vol. 3-1, Evangelischer Verlag A. G., Zollikon/Zürich, 1945.

6J. T. Wiersma, *De Schepping*, Boekencentrum, The Hague, 1949.

7Hendrik A. Brongers, *De Scheppingstradities by de Profeten* (Ph.D. Thesis), H. J. Paris, Amsterdam, 1945.

CHAPTER FOUR

The Proclamation of Jahweh
As Creator

1. The Text. Gen. 2:4b-25 (J).

(4b) In the day that the Lord God made the earth and the heavens, (5) And every plant of the field before it was in the earth, and every herb of the field before it grew: for the Lord God had not caused it to rain upon the earth, and there was not a man to till the ground. (6) But there went up a mist from the earth, and watered the whole face of the ground. (7) And the Lord God formed man of the dust of the ground, and breathed into his nostrils the breath of life; and man became a living soul.

(8) And the Lord God planted a garden eastward in Eden; and there he put the man whom he had formed. (9) And out of the ground made the Lord God to grow every tree that is pleasant to the sight, and good for food; the tree of life also in the midst of the garden, and the tree of knowledge of good and evil.

(10) And a river went out of Eden to water the garden; and from thence it was parted, and became into four heads. (11) The name of the first is Pison: that is it which compasseth the whole land of Havilah, where there is gold; (12) And the

gold of that land is good: there is bdellium and the onyx stone. (13) And the name of the second river is Gihon: the same is it that compasseth the whole land of Ethiopia. (14) And the name of the third river is Hiddekel: that is it which goeth toward the east of Assyria. And the fourth river is Euphrates.

(15) And the Lord God took the man, and put him into the garden of Eden to dress it and to keep it. (16) And the Lord God commanded the man, saying, Of every tree of the garden thou mayest freely eat: (17) But of the tree of knowledge of good and evil, thou shalt not eat of it: for in the day that thou eatest thereof thou shalt surely die.

(18) And the Lord God said, It is not good that man should be alone; I will make him an help meet for him. (19) And out of the ground the Lord God formed every beast of the field, and every fowl of the air; and brought them unto Adam to see what he would call them: and whatsoever Adam called every living creature, that was the name thereof. (20) And Adam gave names to all cattle, and to the fowl of the air, and to every beast of the field; but for Adam there was not found an help meet for him.

(21) And the Lord God caused a deep sleep to fall upon Adam, and he slept: and he took one of his ribs, and closed up the flesh instead thereof; (22) And the rib, which the Lord God had taken from man, made he a woman, and brought her unto the man. (23) And Adam said, This is now bone of my bones, and flesh of my flesh: she shall be called Woman, because she was taken out of Man, (24) Therefore shall a man leave his father and his mother, and shall cleave unto his wife: and they shall be one flesh. (25) And they were both naked, the man and his wife, and were not ashamed.

Notes:

1. Verses 5 and 6 are dependent clauses. The independent clause thus reads: "In the day that the Lord God made the earth and the heavens, the Lord God formed man of the dust of the ground, . . ."

2. Since "Adam" is here not a personal name, the word should be replaced by "the man."

2. Interpretation of the text.

This section of Genesis belongs to J, which means that it is not doctrine, nor sacred teaching but primarily *proclamation* of Jahweh as creator. In its basic aim there is full agreement with Gen. 1, but it differs strongly from Gen. 1 in the way the story is developed. Not the creation of heaven and earth stands in the foreground, but the creation of the man and the woman forms the center of the story. The view does not sweep over heaven and earth but rests on the garden of Eden.

Also the literary approach of the two accounts of creation differ widely. P gives a very logical and systematic account of what it means that God is creator; there are no hidden meanings nor symbolisms. J however, tells an imaginative story full of symbolisms and hidden meanings. Things are often not spelled out in detail but are merely hinted at. This gives the story on the one hand a much more primitive character than Gen. 1, whereas on the other hand it gives it a poetic quality that greatly contributes to its impact.

The beginning of the story is somewhat confused in the King James version, since it treats Gen. 2:4a and 2:4b as one sentence and understands some dependent clauses as independent ones. We follow the Revised Standard Version to clarify the difficulty. It reads: "In the day that the Lord God made the earth and the heavens, when no plant of the field was yet in the earth and no herb of the field had yet sprung up—for the Lord God had not caused it to rain upon the earth, and there was no man to till the ground; but a mist went up from the earth and watered the whole face of the ground—then the Lord God formed man of dust from the ground, and breathed into his nostrils the breath of life; and man became a living being" (Gen. 2:4b-7).

Since the independent clause is: "In the day that the Lord God made the earth and the heavens . . . then the Lord God formed man of the dust of the ground," it can be concluded that J's creation account starts with the creation of *man*. The order of the story is thus reversed, man is created *first* and the animals are created *later*[3-4].

There is nothing peculiar in that man is formed of the dust of the ground, and there is nothing degrading in it. As a farmer in Palestine saw things, practically everything of importance came from the ground. For that reason it should be considered quite natural that man is made of the ground. Moreover, the author tries to depict the close relationship between the man and the soil.

This is done by means of an interesting word play that could not be preserved in the English translation. In the original the word "Adam" is used for "man" and the word "Adama" is used for the "field" from which man was taken. The story thus states: "Adam was taken from the Adama." This word play gives an answer to the question: "Why is man so intimately connected to the field?" The answer is: "Because he was taken from it, Adam and the Adama belong together." In addition, the word play sets the scene for the later verdict "from the Adama thou wast taken, to the Adama thou shalt return" (Gen. 3:19).

A literary form in which a question is answered by a story is known as an "aetiology." J's account of creation and fall is full of such aetiologies, as will be seen later. But more than an aetiology is at stake here, for in it God is proclaimed as man's creator. Moreover, the story emphasizes in this manner that the farmer, his field and his work are part of God's good creation.

In P's creation account God is often compared to a great army commander who gives the command and it is carried out. J's creation account compares God to a sculptor who models the man, and later the animals, out of the dust of the field and then brings them to life. This should not be taken literally. J does not literally conceive of God as working with His hands or possessing a body like a man, that would be contrary to J's actual conception of God[2] (A. Richardson). The picture is used to present the abstract idea of man's creation in a concrete form.

Gen. 2:4b-25 uses the name "Jahweh Elohim" for God. As such Gen. 2 is almost unique in the Old Testament. "Jahweh" is the name that J always uses for God. Some Old Testament scholars have suggested that the name Elohim is a later addition to the text to make clear that the God of Chapter 2 is the same as of Chapter 1. The expression would then state the identity: Jahweh = Elohim.

We saw that the word "Adam" means "man" or "the man." In Gen. 2 it is used as a general *name*, not as a *personal* name. For that reason one should read "the man" where the King James version uses the word "Adam." When Adam is used as a general name, it means "man" in general and he is seen as *our representative.* What is said about Adam involves *us.* Adam's creation represents *our* creation, his task represents *our* task, and as we shall see later, *his* marriage relationship represents *our* marriage relationship and *his* sin represents *our* sin. This is inherent in the fact that J's account of creation is *preaching, proclamation.*

Our words "wind," "breath" and "spirit" come from the same word in the original. When the story thus states that "God breathed into man's nostrils the breath of life," the author indicates in the most direct and concrete manner that our life is a gift of God, that our breath is a gift of God and that our spirit is a gift of God.

The word "living soul" means "living being." The Greek concept of "soul," that we often use, was alien to the author and to the readers of Gen. 2. For them man did not "have" a soul, but he "became" a "living soul" when he was brought to life. This Jewish concept of "soul" appears all through the Old Testament.

Now that the independent clause has been dealt with, we turn to the dependent ones. The first one states that before man was created, no plants of the field were in the earth and no herbs of the field had sprung up, because it had not yet rained upon the earth. The beginning, as J sees it, is thus quite different from P's version. There the water and the land were not yet separated in the beginning, here the dry land has not yet been moistened. This indicates a difference in background: P's background is formed by the Babylonian lowlands for which water is always a threat, whereas J's background is given by the Palestinian highlands for which lack of water often spelled calamity.

One would now expect the story to continue as "and God

caused it to rain upon the earth." But instead it states: "a mist went up from the earth." This has caused difficulties in interpretation, for many object to the idea that a mist can "come up from the earth." Some have therefore suggested to interpret "mist" as "ground water." There is no reason either for the objection or for the suggestion. For to a casual observer early morning fog seems indeed to "come up" from the ground, as anyone living in a rural area can testify. This early morning fog leaves dew behind that can moisten "the whole face of the ground." In the highlands of Palestine there were long dry spells, when any moisture for the fields had to come from the dew. For that reason the Old Testament considers the dew to be a most precious gift of God. The Palestine farmer would therefore expect moisture to come from dew and not from rain or ground water, and the story conforms to this expectation.

The work of creation consists in the planting of a beautiful garden, or more correctly a "park." The word "paradise" was originally a Persian word denoting a nobleman's park. This does not imply that God did not *also* create the whole earth and everything in it. On the contrary, the beautiful garden represents *all* of creation, just as Adam represents *us*.

In this garden God puts the man "to dress it and to keep it." God therefore gives man his task: agriculture and horticulture. Man is put to work in a garden that belongs to God. He stands in God's service and his work is God's good gift to him. The storyteller thus emphasizes for his listeners that their work is part of God's good creation, part of God's good plan for man. In the same manner Gen. 2 proclaims to us that *our* work is part of God's good creation. Their work and our work can be seen in another light, as the second part of Gen. 3 will make clear. Nevertheless, it remains important to remember that our work belongs to God's good creation.

The author does not state explicitly that the plants of the field and the herbs of the field were "created," at least not according to the Revised Standard Version. Apparently the text assumes that the "moistening of the face of the ground" took care of this. The trees seem to come up in the same manner. But nothing goes automatically here. If anything "comes up," then it is because God "made" it come up. Again, as in P's account of creation, natural processes and God's creative activity go hand in hand.

The reason why trees are mentioned specifically is that trees were rather scarce in many parts of Palestine and their presence was valued highly. To mention them emphasizes once again how beautiful the garden and how good God's creation is.

Two trees are mentioned specifically: "the tree of life" and "the tree of knowledge of good and evil." What does the introduction of the trees mean? They are apparently used to represent abstract ideas in concrete form.

The tree of life, for example, plays an important part in many mythologies. Its fruits, if taken regularly, give "eternal life" or, to put it less abstractly, "make man live forever" (Gen. 3:22). The mythological tree of life is not introduced for mythological reasons, however, for the story is quite unmythological in its intents. It is introduced to represent the abstract idea of "eternal life" in a concrete form. For the same reason the tree of knowledge is introduced to present the abstract idea of "God's command" in a concrete form.

What does the expression "knowledge of good and evil" mean? It does not refer primarily to a moral background, as one might think at first sight. "Good and evil" in the affirmative sense means "everything" (Gen. 24:50, 31:24, 29; Numbers 24:13; Deut. 1:39; 2 Sam. 13:22, 14:17, 19:36; 1 Kings

3:9). If coupled with a negation it means "nothing."[1] "Knowledge of good and evil" thus means "omniscience."

Knowledge in the Hebrew sense, however, means much more than mere intellectual knowledge. The verb "to know" is often used in the sense of "to experience" or "to become familiar with," so that it can even be used in the sense of "to have sexual relations with." The tree of the knowledge of good and evil symbolizes human experience in its entirety (A. Richardson[2]).

The story is quite vague about the location of the garden. It speaks of "eastward in Eden," but it is not clear whether "Eden" is a place name or another indication of the beauty of the garden (Eden means delight, enchantment, pleasure). Neither does the mentioning of the four rivers solve the problem, even though some of them can be identified. The third and the fourth are, of course, the Tigris and the Euphrates. The second river is thought to refer to the Nubian Nile, since it is said to encompass Ethiopia. For the first river the sea around Arabia or the river Indus have been suggested. Since the four rivers do not come from the same source, the story apparently does not aim at pinpointing the location of the garden. Neither does it try to give lessons in geography.

Most likely the aim is quite different. In a country where water is scarce, the presence of rivers that can water the fields is of the utmost importance. The river going out of Eden and parting into four rivers emphasizes the abundance of the water supply of the garden and hence the beauty of the garden and the goodness of God's creation. The four rivers flowing to all the countries known to the storyteller and his listeners make these countries share in the life-giving water of the garden. This indicates once again that the garden represents *all* of creation, that God is preached as the creator of *all* and that all the world is His *good* creation. Moreover, it emphasizes that what happens *in* the garden is of the utmost importance to the *world*.

God gives the man a command. Actually, the command means that God gives the man a great freedom. He may freely eat of all the trees of the garden except one. And this exception is not made to withhold something essential from man but is part of God's fatherly care. For God knows, what man does not know yet, that the fruit of the tree, that is omniscience, or the fullness of human experience, is not good for man but leads to his downfall. The story puts this abstract idea in the concrete form of the command: not to eat of the tree.

The fullness of human experience includes the experience of death[2]. That is what God in His care withholds from man. For that reason the warning is given: "for in the day that thou eatest thereof thou shalt surely die." The expression "in the day" means "when," so that the warning does not mean that the man will die instantly when he disobeys God's command. The story emphasizes simply that man stands under God's command and that his well-being depends on his obedience to God. Through it the story places the same facts before *us*.

The story does *not* say that man cannot eat of the tree of life. Later, when man is driven out of the garden, he is thereby *prevented* from eating of the tree of life, but that is another story.

The man now has his work and his duty, but he needs more: he needs a *real partner*. This finds its temporary solution in the creation of the animals. These animals are again made out of the ground and are then brought to life, just as in the case of man. Once again God is proclaimed as creator in a manner that the listeners can understand. Once again the close interdependence between the man, the animals and the ground is stressed. Once more God's fatherly care is praised in that He gives man the additional tasks of naming the animals and caring for them.

Ancient thought attached much greater importance to names than we do. Words were more than a means of communication and the use of the appropriate name was anything but arbitrary. Naming an animal properly indicated that one had understood and characterized its properties, that one had established a relationship with it and one's rule over it. Seen in this primitive light, speech is in the first place needed to understand, to order and to rule and only in the second place it is needed for communication. This is sometimes forgotten in modern thinking.

The creation of animals does not alleviate man's need for a *real* partner. They do not overcome man's basic loneliness. For that reason God creates the woman. God does this while the man sleeps. Apparently he must not behold the miracle that God performs for him.

What is a real partner? It is someone like the man but not identical with him. To indicate that the woman is really *like* the man, the story tells that God took one of the man's ribs and made it into a woman. The real partner is there when he awakens from his sleep. Hence the exclamation: "This is now bone of my bones, and flesh of my flesh." For the same reason he gives her the name "wo-man." The original uses a word play that could be preserved in the English translation. The name is more than a mere play of words, however, it gives the essential characterization of the one who is so named. And through the name the man claims and identifies the woman as *his* woman. The two belong to each other and actually complement each other.

The story is an aetiology. To the question: "Why the strong attraction between the sexes?" it answers: "Because they belong together; they were one flesh originally and hence they want to reunite." For that reason the author adds*: "Therefore shall a man leave his father and mother, and shall cleave unto his wife: and they shall be one flesh." But much more than a mere aetiology is meant here; the story hereby claims the man, the woman and their relationship as parts of God's good creation.

Marriage is hereby instituted. The aim of marriage, as seen here, is not the propagation of the human race, as in Gen. 1, but the *partnership* or *relationship* between the sexes. In that respect Gen. 2 is almost unique in the Old Testament, for only the Song of Solomon takes up the same theme. That their relationship is very frankly seen as a *sexual* relationship, is indicated by the expression "and they shall be one flesh." It is seen as God's good gift to them. Their relationship has another side, as becomes clear in the second half of Genesis 3, but it is important to remember the first side too.

This is also a necessary reminder to us. For since the story is preaching, proclamation, it aims at *us* and at *our* marriage relationship. In the past the Christian view of marriage was clouded by two misconceptions:

1. The aim of marriage was too exclusively seen as procreation, not as partnership.

---

*Though J is the author of Gen. 2, this does not mean that Gen. 2 is his *free* creation. He was already bound to the authority of a much older tradition. Only occasionally does one find an expression that can be attributed to the author himself. Some Old Testament scholars, e.g. von Rad[1], hold that this is one of those instances.

2. Sex was often viewed as something to be ashamed of.

Genesis 2 can help in clarifying the Christian view of sex and marriage.

The man and his wife, when created, stood in the right relationship with God and with each other and for that reason the story concludes: "And they were both naked, the man and his wife, and were not ashamed." This has often been interpreted as meaning that they had not yet discovered sex. There is no reason for such an interpretation, for the shame and feeling of nakedness mentioned in Gen. 3 has nothing to do with sex but is a consequence of *sin* and a symbol of *guilt*. They were not ashamed, for they had no guilt[5]. By this ending, the story sets the scene for the drama of the fall told in Gen. 3.

To sum it up, Gen. 2 proclaims the Lord God as creator in a very vivid, direct, unabstract manner. It sees Adam as *our* representative, *his* creation represents *our* creation, *his* God-given task in his work represents *our* God-given task in our work, *his* God-given marriage relationship represents *our* God-given marriage relationship. By telling of the creation of *one* man and *one* woman and the planting of *one* garden, God is proclaimed as the creator of *all*. Despite the difference in scope and content, Gen. 1 and Gen. 2 are thus identical as far as the main ideas are concerned.

Gen. 2 speaks about God in an anthropomorphical manner. This does not indicate a crude, primitive concept of God, as some people think, but is done to speak about God's creative acts in a very concrete manner. This should be a reminder to us that the abstract ways of speaking about God, practiced by some philosophers, may not be very appropriate here. It should not be forgotten, that in the Incarnation God did not become an *idea* but that He became *man*.

Gen. 2 sees the acts of creation as a kind of magic: lifeless forms are brought to life, a woman is made out of a man's rib. But the story does so in order to get a nonmagical message across. It claims Jahweh as the creator of the man, the animals and the woman, and work and marriage as God's institutions. Once that has been understood there is no harm in admitting that the language of Gen. 2 has a magical coloring.

The language of Gen. 2 has a strongly mythological flavor. But it should not be forgotten that Gen. 2 preaches and confesses God as the creator of all and that the mythological language is used either to indicate relationships (between the man and the ground, between the man and the woman) or to express abstract ideas in concrete form (the tree of life, the tree of knowledge, etc.). The language is thus used to get a very unmythological message across. It is therefore wrong to speak of the "myth of Adam's creation" or the "myth of the tree of knowledge" or of the "fable of Adam's rib." Once it has been understood what Gen. 2 aims at in telling the story of creation in this manner, there is no harm in admitting that the language of Gen. 2 is mythologically colored.

Having understood that Gen. 2 is nonmythological in its intent, we have to deal with a few other misconceptions. Gen. 2 is also not an *allegory,* neither is it a *parable.* An allegory* is "a veiled representation, in a figurative story, of a meaning metaphorically implied but not expressly stated." A parable* is "a short fictitious narrative from which a moral or spiritual truth is drawn." Gen. 2 is neither, for it aims at proclaiming God as creator of all. The stories told are neither allegories nor parables, but they are *aetiologies:* questions are answered by

---

*Webster l. c.

giving the creation account the appropriate twist at the appropriate moment.

Gen. 2 offers little opportunity for harmonizing its content with modern science. This is a real asset, for it draws our attention to the *message* that Gen. 2 tries to bring. Thereby it also gives hints how Gen. 1 should be read: one should not crave for harmonization, but listen to its message.

Having understood what Gen. 2 aims at, the following questions must be considered wrong questions:

1—Were the man and the animals indeed made of dust of the ground? That is a wrong question, for the story is told in that way to emphasize the close relationship between the man, the animals and the field. The story is *not* told to give us lessons in biology.

2—Was there a real garden of Eden? That is a wrong question, for the garden represents *all* of creation. The garden is singled out to confess in the most explicit manner that the Lord God is the creator of *all*. The story is not told to give us lessons in geography.

3—Was the woman really made of Adam's rib? This is a wrong question, for the story is told in the manner to emphasize that the woman is the man's real partner. The two are meant for each other and actually complement each other. The story is not told to give us lessons in anatomy.

These questions are *wrong* questions because in them we project *our* problems into the story instead of trying to grasp its meaning. Right questions are those that stay within the atmosphere and spirit of Gen. 2 and elucidate its meaning. We tried to do that in our discussion.

REFERENCES:

[1]Gerhard von Rad, see Chapter 3.
[2]Alan Richardson, see Chapter 3.
[3]Hellmuth Frey, see Chapter 3.
[4]Dietrich Bonhoeffer, see Chapter 3.
[5]Karl Barth, see Chapter 3.

CHAPTER FIVE

The Story of Human Sin

1. The Text. Gen. 3 (J).

(1) *Now the serpent was more subtil than any beast of the field which the Lord God had made. And he said unto the woman, Yea, hath God said, Ye shall not eat of every tree of the garden?* (2) *And the woman said unto the serpent, We may eat of the fruit of the trees of the garden:* (3) *But of the fruit of the tree which is in the midst of the garden, God hath said, Ye shall not eat of it, neither shall ye touch it, lest ye die.* (4) *And the serpent said unto the woman, Ye shall not surely die:* (5) *For God doth know that in the day ye eat thereof, then your eyes shall be opened, and ye shall be as gods, knowing good and evil.* (6) *And when the woman saw that the tree was good for food, and that it was pleasant to the eyes, and a tree to be desired to make one wise, she took of the fruit thereof, and did eat, and gave also unto her husband with her; and he did eat.* (7) *And the eyes of both of them were opened, and they knew that they were naked; and they sewed fig leaves together, and made themselves aprons.*

(8) *And they heard the voice of the Lord God walking in the garden in the cool of the day: and Adam and his wife hid*

themselves from the presence of the Lord God amongst the trees of the garden. (9) And the Lord God called unto Adam, and said unto him, Where art thou? (10) And he said, I heard thy voice in the garden, and I was afraid, because I was naked; and I hid myself. (11) And he said, Who told thee that thou wast naked? Hast thou eaten of the tree, whereof I commanded thee that thou shouldest not eat? (12) And the man said, The woman whom thou gavest to be with me, she gave me of the tree, and I did eat. (13) And the Lord God said unto the woman, What is this that thou hast done? And the woman said, The serpent beguiled me, and I did eat.

(14) And the Lord God said unto the serpent, Because thou hast done this, thou art cursed above all cattle, and above every beast of the field; upon thy belly shalt thou go, and dust shalt thou eat all the days of thy life: (15) And I will put enmity between thee and the woman, and between thy seed and her seed; it shall bruise thy head, and thou shalt bruise his heel. (16) Unto the woman he said, I will greatly multiply thy sorrow and thy conception; in sorrow thou shalt bring forth children; and thy desire shall be to thy husband, and he shall rule over thee. (17) And unto Adam he said, Because thou hast harkened unto the voice of thy wife, and hast eaten of the tree, of which I commanded thee, saying, Thou shalt not eat of it: cursed is the ground for thy sake; in sorrow shalt thou eat of it all the days of thy life; (18) Thorns also and thistles shall it bring forth to thee; and thou shalt eat the herb of the field; (19) In the sweat of thy face shalt thou eat bread, till thou return unto the ground; for out of it wast thou taken: for dust thou art, and unto dust shalt thou return.

(20) And Adam called his wife's name Eve; because she was the mother of all living. (21) Unto Adam also and to his wife did the Lord God make coats of skins, and clothed them.

(22) And the Lord God said, Behold, the man is become as one of us, to know good and evil: and now, lest he put forth his hand, and take also of the tree of life, and eat, and live forever: (23) Therefore the Lord God sent him forth from the garden of Eden, to till the ground from whence he was taken. (24) So he drove out the man; and he placed at the east of the garden of Eden Cherubims, and a flaming sword which turned every way, to keep the way of the tree of life.

Note:

Since "Adam" is here not a personal name, it should be replaced by "the man."

2. Discussion.

Gen. 3 belongs to J and is the immediate continuation of Gen. 2. That this section belongs to J means that one can expect a story told in an imaginative manner full of symbolisms, hidden meanings and aetiologies, stories that give a deep insight into the human condition.

Gen. 2 precedes Gen. 3. This indicates that God's good creation comes *before* human sin. God is not the author of sin, but man is responsible for it. Sin is not part of God's good creation but disturbs and soils it.

Gen. 3 preaches that man is a sinner. The story has a very strong personal element; it does not intend to demonstrate a *general* truth, but it aims a very particular message at its listeners. It tells them not: "man is sinful," but: "you are a sinner."

The beginning of the story speaks of temptation. Since no abstract ideas are used, temptation is pictured as a speaking serpent. Why a serpent? Because in Semitic tradition the serpent is proverbial for cunning craftiness. A serpent has something stealthy and frightening in its movement. Just as it moves silently and shows up unexpectedly, so temptation falls upon man suddenly. The temptation is pictured as a *speaking* serpent, because the importance is in the *words* that are used and in the *ideas* that are generated in the woman as a consequence.

One should not consider the speaking serpent as a *personification* of temptation. The serpent remains far too much in the background for that. It only gives the initial suggestions that make man see possibilities that had hitherto escaped notice. But these possibilities are *man's* possibilities, their execution is *man's* responsibility and the guilt that results is *man's* guilt. The speaking serpent puts these hidden processes in a concrete form that allows one to visualize them.

For the same reason it is better to speak of "temptation" than of a "tempter." And the serpent should not be seen as "Satan." According to Alan Richardson[2] the concept of a personal devil did not arise until after the exile, that is, long after the J-account was written. Only in the discussion of the curse upon the serpent (Gen. 3:14) does it seem necessary to take into account that there is a tempter behind the temptation.

The serpent confuses the woman by misquoting God's command. It asks: "Has God forbidden to eat of the fruit of *all trees?*" The woman answers correctly: "We may eat of the fruit of all trees except one." But then she adds: "God has said that if we eat of it or touch it, we shall die." This is an overstatement of the command, for she adds that the tree should not even be *touched.* It is as if she has a foreboding for the weakness of her position and tries to overcompensate for it by overstating the command.

She now leaves herself open for the attack. First a partial denial is made of what God had said, then doubt is cast upon God's motives and finally an attractive picture is painted of what disobedience will bring. Is not that the natural history of *all* temptation?

The serpent suggests that the threat of death is a hollow one. Moreover, God did not forbid man to eat of the tree of good and evil out of fatherly goodness but in order to preserve His divinity for Himself. "Knowledge of good and evil," or the "fulness of human experience" is not something to be dreaded but something to be desired. Who does not want to find this fullness and be as a god to himself? The serpent thus caters to man's pride, to man's desire to assert himself and to man's striving of putting himself in God's place. His argumentations are a curious mixture of truth and falsehood. They are quite similar to the argumentations that *we* give when we want to rationalize *our* disobedience. For that reason Richardson[2] says: "How clearly J perceives that our 'reasons' are rationalizations, that pride is the father of doubt."

The woman is allured by the possibilities that have been opened up. Who does not want to enter into the fullness of human experience? Who does not want to take life in his own hands, decide for himself, and "be as a god" to himself? All of a sudden obedience to God's command seems dull and uninteresting and disobedience seems to be a most alluring option. The woman sees for herself that what was said by the serpent seems to be true. For that reason the story continues: "And when the woman saw that the tree was good for food, and that it was pleasant to the eyes, and a tree to be desired to make one wise, she took of the fruit thereof, and did eat." The temptation has been successful.

Popular interpretation has identified the tree of knowledge with an apple tree and its fruit with an apple. This comes from the fact that the Latin words for "an apple" (malum) and for "an evil" (malum) are identical. But there is no need for such an identification. The fruit enters into the story to put God's command in a concrete form and to picture the alluring aspects of temptation.

The woman does not keep her disobedience for herself but she lets the man share in it. She eats of the fruit and she gives to her husband and he eats too. Disobedience becomes even more attractive if it is shared with others. Sharing makes it also more bearable.

The result is not as temptation promised, it never is, but God's warning becomes a fact. It is true what the serpent said: their eyes are opened and they know for the first time everything (good and evil). But what comes in view now is not a panorama of man's tremendous possibilities. What they experience instead is that they stand *guilty* before God, that they have *sinned* against God and that they can expect God's *punishment*.

The story pictures the discovery of their guilt by stating that they saw "their nakedness." The man and the woman are afraid that by seeing their nakedness God will see that they stand guilty. They sew fig leaves together and make themselves aprons, to hide their guilt before God. But they know that this is insufficient. Hence, when they hear God approaching, they hide themselves before Him among the trees of the garden.

Popular interpretations, and sometimes even not so popular ones (D. Bonhoeffer[4]) have maintained that the story alludes here to the discovery of sex. When the man and the woman become aware of each other's nakedness, they say, lust is kindled in them and correspondingly their shame is awakened. This is completely alien to the text, for nowhere does the story give any hint about sexual desire. Their sense of nakedness represents their feeling of *guilt*. The man and the woman are not ashamed for each other, but, because of their guilt, they stand ashamed before God. They do not make themselves aprons to hide their sex characteristics for each other and to hide themselves from the lustful eyes of the other, or of others, but to cover their guilt before God. They do not hide *from each other*, but *together they hide before God*.

Before continuing it might be advisable to pause and ask questions. We have heard what the story said. Do we now know how sin came into the world? Contrary to popular opinion, this is not the case. Gen. 3 does not tell us where temptation comes from; suddenly it is there with all its beguiling power. Gen. 3 does not give a "theory" of sin but states in a very concrete and direct manner the *nature* of sin. And it proclaims *us* as sinners.

Sin is a consequence of yielding to temptation, here pictured by the speaking serpent. Sin is disobedience against God's concrete commands, here represented by the command concerning the forbidden fruit. Sin is rebellion against God's love and care, here pictured as the desire to obtain what God in His love and care has withheld from man. Sin is attempting to be independent of God and desiring to be like Him, sovereign master over everything (good and evil). Gen. 3 thus tells of the prototype of *all* sin.

Since Gen. 3 is preaching, proclamation, its message also aims at *us* and condemns *us*. For the man and the woman are seen as our *representatives*. The command given to them represents the command given to *us,* their sin represents *our* sin, their guilt represents *our* guilt. We are *like them,* we fell *in them.*

The problem of sin can be further elucidated by considering the man and the woman as our ancestors, as the first pair. Seen in that light, the story proclaims to us that sin goes to the *beginning* of man's existence. Hardly was man created, hardly had he received from God his existence, his task and his wife, or he sinned. But even in this context the emphasis is not on the succession of generations. That problem is dealt with later.

In the apocryphal "First Book of Adam and Eve,"[5] chapters 34, 37, the idea that sin goes to the beginning of man's existence is illustrated as follows. Adam was created at the third hour of the sixth day. At the end of the third hour a deep sleep came over him and the woman was created. The transgression took place at the sixth hour and at the ninth hour of the sixth day they were driven out of the garden.

On a personal level this leads to the confession that sin goes to the root of *our* existence. This is most drastically expressed in Psalm 51: "Behold, I was shapen in iniquity; and in sin did my mother conceive me." This does not mean, as it has sometimes been understood, that there is something intrinsically evil in the sex relationship. Neither should it be understood as a *general* statement about sin. It is a *personal confession* of sin; it expresses on a personal level what is stated in Gen. 3.

Gen. 3 does not teach the doctrine of "man's depravity." In this doctrine the church expresses man's wickedness over against God. We find it, however, in the flood story and in many other places in the Old Testament. For example, in Gen. 6:5, which belongs to J, it is stated: "And God saw that the wickedness of man was great in the earth, and that every imagination of the thoughts of his heart was only evil continually." In Gen. 6:11, which belongs to P, we read: "The earth also was corrupt before God, and the earth was filled with violence." This wickedness, this corruption, this violence is the continuation of the sin that is described in Gen. 3.

The P-account does not have a story of the fall. Nevertheless, it too considers man a sinner as Gen. 6 clearly indicates. This is another indication that one should not stress the causal connection between Adam's sin and our sin. Adam is our representative.

Theologians have tried to elucidate the connection between Adam's sin and our sin by introducing an argument based on *heredity*. They thus state that since the first pair sinned, their descendants became sinners by heredity. "Adam's sin" then becomes "hereditary sin" (Erbsünde in German). This is confusing. For according to Gen. 3 man is responsible for his sin, whereas it is hard to see how man can be held responsible for his heredity. This difficulty is avoided if heredity arguments are not introduced at this point.

Rather than using the word "Erbsünde," we should use the word "original sin." Original sin does not so much refer to a sin of Adam as to a *condition*. It is the condition that "man is born without a true love or fear of God." This condition is inherited, not by heredity, but by being in the same condition as those who went before us. Adam's descendants share in Adam's condition of living outside the garden of Eden, outside of God's nearness.

The question is often asked: "Did the serpent actually speak?" That is a wrong question. The serpent pictures temptation and it speaks to plant the question: "Did God really say this?" into the woman's mind. It is not the aim to demonstrate that serpents have the ability to speak.

It is often asked: "Should not the eating of the fruit of the tree of knowledge be seen as man's emancipation to full humanity?" Some people hold indeed to the ideal that man should become his own master and king, deciding for himself what is good and evil without being bound by "old taboos and superstitions." It is what the serpent promises. But Gen. 3 stresses the exact opposite. "Good" in the Biblical sense is what God wills and "evil" is what goes against God's will. Man does not become "emancipated" by liberating himself from God's rule over him, for that brings his downfall. Man becomes truly emancipated by staying close to God, by "walking with God" as the Bible says about Enoch or by "walking before God" as the Bible tells about Abraham and other great believers of the Old Testament.

After they have sinned, the man and the woman hide themselves from God. But God does not leave them alone. He calls the sinners, to condemn, to punish and to forgive them. And the man answers God: "I was afraid, because I was naked; and I hid myself." God then asks whether he has perhaps eaten of the forbidden fruit. Here would be the point to confess right out and say: "Yes, I did." But instead the man tries to shift the blame upon the woman and indirectly upon the Lord God Himself by answering: "The woman whom thou gavest to be with me, gave me of the tree." Here is indicated how sin not only disrupts the relationship between man and God but also disrupts the solidarity between the man and the woman.

God does not deal with the man's accusation for the time being, but addresses the woman: "What hast thou done?" And she, again, does not confess right out but tries to shift the blame upon the serpent by answering: "The serpent beguiled me."

Just as covering their guilt by putting on fig leaves and by hiding before God does not help, so shifting the blame upon somebody else does not work either. Guilt cannot be hidden or shifted, but it must be *forgiven*. But condemnation of sin and punishment of sin come before forgiveness.

God takes up the woman's excuse by first condemning the serpent. The serpent is cursed to go upon his belly and to eat the dust of the ground. The story does not try to give an aetiological explanation of the fact that serpents crawl on the ground. Neither does it try to explain why people do not like snakes. It also does not try to postulate a deadly enmity between serpents and mankind. Neither is the story interested in early stages of snake development when these animals walked upright or had legs.

As said before, the serpent represents temptation, and it is here the *tempter,* who is behind the temptation, who is cursed for having tempted the man and the woman. And the crawling serpent, going on its belly and seemingly eating the dust of the ground is forever the symbol of the tempter and his curse. The listeners can *see* this symbol and are thereby reminded of the reality of man's sinfulness.

The story continues with a statement that the Christian church has always considered as a great promise of Messianic character: "And I will put enmity between thee and the woman, and between thy seed and her seed; it shall bruise thy head, and thou shalt bruise his heel." (Gen. 3:15). Most Old Testament scholars, e.g. von Rad[1], deny that this is a Messianic prophecy. To them the statement means in the first place an aetiology. It lays bare the background of the seemingly endless and hopeless struggle between man and temptation, man and sin or, to put it in a more abstract way: the struggle between good and evil in man.

This is certainly an aspect of Gen. 3 that should not be ignored. But is it the only aspect? Does not the text of Gen. 3 imply that the statement can be seen as a promise? Does not the story tell that the struggle is set by *God?* And does not this mean that God is more than a mere onlooker?

To me this would seem to be the case. True enough, the struggle is unequal: the tempter is strong and man is weak. But though the tempter will tempt, man will resist. God will see to that. And that means that not every temptation will be followed. Some will be rejected. The statement that it is *God* who sets the struggle, implies that the situation is not hopeless: victories over sin are promised with God's help.

Is Gen. 3:15 a Messianic promise? Not directly, it would seem. In that respect the Old Testament scholars are right. But in my opinion it is permissible for the Christian church to apply its knowledge of Christ to Gen. 3:15. For what is true for man in a limited sense is indeed true for Jesus Christ. For He, through suffering, death and resurrection, has won the victory over the tempter and over sin. New revelation sheds light on old promises.

Of course, we would not know of this if Christ had not come. Only *after* Christ has come can one connect Him to Gen. 3:15 and see the text in Messianic light. In this respect the restraint of the Old Testament scholars is well taken.

Their objections hold even more strongly for the effort to see the reference to the "seed of the woman" as the prophecy of the virgin birth. If we would not know about the virgin birth from elsewhere, we would never guess it from Gen. 3:15.

Knowing about it, however, there is no objection in making a connection with Gen. 3:15; the expression "seed of the woman" can bring into remembrance what we know about the virgin birth from elsewhere. One should be careful, however, not to read too much into a single passage of scripture; the remaining parts were not written for nothing!

Next the woman is spoken to. She is not cursed. But instead the relationship between her and her husband is put in a double light. The story answers aetiologically the questions: "Why these discomforts of pregnancy and the pain of childbirth? Why does the good marriage relationship established by God result in man's rule over her?" It lays bare the grounds for this.

To conceive and to give birth are still joyful occasions. But there is another and darker side to the picture and this darker side is seen as a sign, a reminder, of the fall into sin. The relationship is primarily an aetiological one rather than a causal one. It would go too far to say that the discomforts of pregnancy and the pain of childbirth are seen as *outright consequences of sin*. It is better to say that they are seen as *indicators of the fall*.

Marriage is still God's good gift to man and what was said about it in Gen. 2 remains true. But there is another and darker side to the picture and this darker side is seen as a sign, a reminder of the fall into sin. Again the relationship is foremost an aetiological one rather than a causal one. Man's rule over the woman is not a *consequence of sin* and it would be wrong to conclude that it is justified by the fall. It is better to say that the way in which the woman's desire for her husband results in his rule over her is seen as an *indicator of the fall*.

These indicators of the fall are not put in an abstract manner, but appear in the most concrete form. Everyday occurrences in the lives of the women listeners are taken. The basic facts of their lives: pregnancy, childbirth, desire for her husband, and his rule over her, are used to make the fall clearly visible and concrete for the women listeners. The story makes the basic facts of their lives cry out that they are sinners.

Finally the man is addressed by God. First of all his excuse for his sin is dealt with. His effort to shift the blame upon the woman is of no avail; he is held responsible. He *knew* God's command and should not have listened to the woman.

The man is not cursed, but the *ground* is cursed instead. Man's activity, his work in the field for his daily bread now appears in a double light. The story answers aetiologically the questions: "Why the hard struggle for the daily bread? Why this backbreaking work? Why the fight against the thorns and thistles?" It lays bare the ground for this.

What Gen. 2 said about man's task has not changed. Man's work still remains God's good gift to him. But the story now points to a darker side of the picture: the often hard and seemingly hopeless struggle for existence. And all this is seen as a sign, a reminder, of the fall into sin. Again the relationship is primarily an aetiological rather than a causal one. The story does not say that the thorns, thistles and other obnoxious weeds and the hardships of man's life as a farmer are *direct* consequences of sin. Rather they are seen as *indicators* of the fall. Again these indicators of the fall appear in the most concrete form; the story makes the basic facts of the farmer's life cry out that he is a sinner.

There is another aspect to this. As will be seen in a moment, the indicators of the fall are a sign that man does no longer live in the garden of Eden, that is, that the original close relationship between God and man no longer exists.

"Till thou return unto the ground..." When man's death is mentioned, a concept developed in Gen. 2 comes back into view. Man was taken from the ground, unto the ground he shall return. He was made of dust, unto dust he shall return. The story of man's creation, as told in Gen. 2, was put in that manner to prepare for this turn of events.

Many Old Testament scholars point to the dark ending of the story. Gloom hangs over the existence of both man and woman. Birth, hard, backbreaking work on an unfriendly soil, ending in death, that is the life of the man. Birth, marriage, pregnancy, childbirth, man's rule over her, and finally death, that is the life of the woman. Is there then no hope left?

Hope comes not from what man *sees,* but from what God *does.* Though man has broken his close relationship with God through his disobedience, and deserves to be left alone by God, God continues to speak to man and re-establish connection with him. The stern judgment of Gen. 3:14-19 is not meant to drive him away from God's mercy, but to draw him toward it. This judgment is the very sign that man is still the object of God's love and care. Judgment and grace are here inseparable.

The punishment can also be seen as the means by which God keeps man from believing that he can find the ground of his being, or his rest and peace, in creation. Creation cannot satisfy man, but only the creator can. It can thus be said that the punishment drives man back to the creator.

That the man and the woman are forgiven follows from the fact that God clothes them with coats of skin. They do not receive these coats to shelter them against inclement weather or to shelter them against lustful eyes. They receive them to *cover their guilt*. When *they* tried to cover themselves with fig leaves, that did not help them. But when God covers them, their guilt *is* covered, *is* forgiven. The story does not try to convey the idea that skins provide better coverage than fig leaves. It implies instead that *God* must take away their guilt by covering (= forgiving) it*, man cannot do it himself.

God clothed the man and the woman in animal skins. To obtain these skins, animals had to be killed. It is therefore sometimes said that the story makes here a reference to the institution of animal sacrifice. It is at best an oblique reference, however, the aim is not to establish the practice of animal sacrifice but to tell the man and the woman that they are forgiven.

The man gives his wife the proud name: "mother of all living." Is this a sign of man's continuing willfulness and pride over and against God, as some interpreters think? The most obvious reason for this name is that a new situation has arisen: human history, as we know it, starts. This new situation has to be met by a new and appropriate name that adequately characterizes it. And it cannot be denied that the name "mother of all living" describes the new situation quite well.

But can the new name not also be seen as an indication that the man *believes* in God's forgiveness? It would seem so. For life is not only a sorrowful venture because of God's severe judgment; God is still with him, man is not left alone. For that reason life can go on in hope and it is worth living. The new name "mother of all living" expresses that.

But forgiveness does not mean that the punishment is not

---

*Compare Psalm 32:1: "Blessed is he whose transgression is forgiven, whose sin is covered."

carried out. The language becomes very solemn; God is introduced as speaking in a plural "us."* The punishment, already announced, is now carried out. Man is banished from the garden of Eden and driven out from God's nearness. It is thus Biblical to relate man's condition to the fact that he lives outside of the garden of Eden, outside of God's nearness. He did so not by accident but by deliberate choice, even though he was not fully aware of what this choice entailed.

By being driven out of the garden, man is prevented from eating of the tree of life and living forever. He is no longer in a position to "grab" eternal life for himself. To obtain it, it must be *given* to him. But that is written in another book.

Some theologians maintain that man's death is unnatural. Genesis 3 does not support this view. True enough, in the garden of Eden man could live forever, by eating of the tree of life. After having been driven out of the garden, nature takes its course and man must ultimately die.

The Apostle Paul states: "For the wages of sin is death; but the gift of God is eternal life through Jesus Christ our Lord." (Rom. 6:26.) The first half of this sentence is often seen as establishing the causal relationship between sin and death. Paul, however, wants to contrast the fruits of man's sin with the fruits of God's grace.

The road back from sin to the original guiltless relationship is blocked. The story expresses this by putting Cherubims (angel-like beings) and a flaming sword (lightning?) at the entrance of the garden, to block the path to it. It takes more than man's power to re-establish the relationship once more. But that is part of another story.

---

*Both J and P make use of this plural when the situation warrants it, it is not a peculiarity of only one of the two traditions.

The relationship between God and man has changed, but it is not fully broken. God is not as near to him as in the garden, but God has not left him either. God continues to act on man's behalf by interceding for him and by showing His gracious will toward him.

Human history, as the Old Testament sees it, is the story of human sin, human hardship and tribulation. But it is also the place where God acts on man's behalf and where God's gracious will toward man is manifested.

REFERENCES:

[1]Gerhard von Rad, see Chapter 3.

[2]Alan Richardson, see Chapter 3.

[3]Hellmuth Frey, see Chapter 3.

[4]Dietrich Bonhoeffer, see Chapter 3.

[5]E.g. in: *The Lost Books of the Bible and the Forgotten Books of Eden*, The World Publishing Company, Cleveland, 1926.

CHAPTER SIX

The Spreading of Sin — the Two Ways

1. The Text. Gen. 4 and 5:29 (J).

(1) And Adam knew Eve his wife; and she conceived, and bare Cain, and said, I have gotten a man from the Lord. (2) And she again bare his brother Abel. And Abel was a keeper of sheep, but Cain was a tiller of the ground. (3) And in process of time it came to pass, that Cain brought of the fruit of the ground an offering unto the Lord. (4) And Abel, he also brought of the firstlings of his flock and of the fat thereof. And the Lord had respect unto Abel and to his offering: (5) But unto Cain and to his offering he had not respect. And Cain was very wroth, and his countenance fell. (6) And the Lord said unto Cain, Why art thou wroth? and why is thy countenance fallen? (7) If thou doest well, shalt thou not be accepted? and if thou doest not well, sin lieth at the door. And unto thee shall be his desire, and thou shalt rule over him. (8) And Cain talked with Abel his brother: and it came to pass, when they were in the field, that Cain rose up against Abel his brother, and slew him.

(9) And the Lord said unto Cain, Where is Abel thy brother? And he said, I know not: Am I my brother's keeper? (10) And he said, What hast thou done? the voice of thy brother's blood crieth unto me from the ground. (11) And now

*art thou cursed from the earth, which hath opened her mouth
to receive thy brother's blood from thy hand; (12) When thou
tillest the ground, it shall not henceforth yield unto thee her
strength; a fugitive and a vagabond shalt thou be in the earth.
(13) And Cain said unto the Lord, My punishment is greater
than I can bear. (14) Behold, thou hast driven me out this day
from the face of the earth; and from thy face shall I be hid;
and I shall be a fugitive and a vagabond in the earth; and it
shall come to pass, that every one that findeth me shall slay
me. (15) And the Lord said unto him, Therefore whosoever
slayeth Cain, vengeance shall be taken on him sevenfold. And
the Lord set a mark upon Cain, lest any finding him should kill
him. (16) And Cain went out from the presence of the Lord,
and dwelt in the land of Nod, on the east of Eden.*

---

*(17) And Cain knew his wife; and she conceived, and bare
Enoch: and he builded a city, and called the name of the city,
after the name of his son, Enoch. (18) And unto Enoch was
born Irad: and Irad begat Mehujael: and Mehujael begat
Methusael: and Methusael begat Lamech. (19) And Lamech
took unto him two wives: the name of the one was Adah, and
the name of the other Zillah. (20) And Adah bare Jabal: he
was the father of such as dwell in tents, and of such as have
cattle. (21) And his brother's name was Jubal: he was the
father of all such as handle the harp and organ. (22) And
Zillah, she also bare Tubalcain, an instructor of every artificer
in brass and iron: and the sister of Tubalcain was Naamah.*

*(23) And Lamech said unto his wives, Adah and Zillah,
Hear my voice; ye wives of Lamech, hearken unto my speech:
for I have slain a man to my wounding, and a young man to*

my hurt. (24) If Cain shall be avenged sevenfold, truly Lamech seventy and sevenfold.

---

(25) And Adam knew his wife again; and she bare a son, and called his name Seth: For God, said she, hath appointed me another seed in stead of Abel, whom Cain slew. (26) And to Seth, to him also there was born a son; and he called his name Enos: then began men to call upon the name of the Lord. . . . 5:29. And he (Lamech) called his (son's) name Noah, saying, This same shall comfort us concerning our work and toil of our hands, because of the ground which the Lord hath cursed.

(The words between parentheses were added for clarification.)

2. Discussion.

The chapter does not form a unity in its present form. Gen. 4:1-16, the story of Cain and Abel, forms one section. The second section, Gen. 4:17-24, the list of Cain's descendants, is quite different. The third section, Gen. 4:25-26, to which Gen. 5:29 also belongs, is quite different from the second one.

Those who adhere to the three-tradition theory, consider the whole chapter as belonging to J. Those who hold to the four-tradition theory assume that Gen. 4:17-24 belongs to L and was later joined to J. That something like this must be the case follows from two important discrepancies between Gen. 4:1-16 and Gen. 4:17-24.

a. In Gen. 4:1-16 we hear nothing of Cain's wife, whereas in Gen. 4:17-24 Cain has a wife.

b. In Gen. 4:1-16 Cain is a restless wanderer, in Gen. 4:17-24 he is the builder of a city.

Probably the Biblical writer knew about these discrepancies as well as, or better than, we do. Apparently he preferred to leave them there. It is likely that he did not consider himself as having the freedom to bridge the gaps. Probably the text already had sufficient authority to him to prevent him doing so. For the same reason he did not have the freedom to amend the text by telling how Cain got his wife.

But there is another good possibility. Perhaps the Biblical writer was not bothered so much by small discrepancies as we are. He joined the two texts together because of what they had in common, not because of their differences. Both Gen. 4:1-16 and Gen. 4:17-24 tell of the spreading of human sin and indicate that it is possible either to lead a life acceptable to God or a life unacceptable to God.

Gen. 4:25-26 and Gen. 5:29 forms part of J's genealogy of Adam up to Noah. In its present form it is only fragmentary. The main part of J's genealogy of Adam has been replaced by P's genealogy of Adam which is given in Gen. 5 minus verse 29. J's genealogy of Adam fits with the remainder of Chapter 4 by sheer contrast.

2a. The story of Cain and Abel (Gen. 4:1-16)

Human history, as we know it, takes its course. Eve gives birth to her first-born son Cain and exclaims: "I have gotten a man with (?) the Lord!" The exact meaning of the words is not quite clear, but through them one hears the pride of motherhood. After that she gives birth to his brother Abel. The word "Abel" means "breath" or "vanity," a dark hint of his short life and of the tragedy that is going to occur.

The story does not tell anything about their youth, but starts immediately with their occupations as young adults. Abel becomes a shepherd and Cain becomes a farmer. Again, the story does not dwell on their work either. The next scene sees both bringing their offerings to the Lord. Cain brings an offering of his fruits of the ground and Abel brings of the firstlings of the flock.

It is not clear what the occasion of the offering is, whether it is considered to be a thank offering or whether there is another reason. The important thing is that both bring an offering *to the Lord* and both do so *separately*. In all outward appearances both do the same thing, but the results are quite different: the Lord accepts Abel's offering but does not accept Cain's offering. This starts the chain of events that leads to the murder of Abel.

The story does not say why the one offering was accepted and the other rejected; it simply states that this was the case. Some interpreters have suggested that the bloody offering was more acceptable to God than the unbloody offering. But that does not seem reasonable since Cain had no bloody offerings to offer. Others[1] have indicated that it is God's free will to accept or to reject: "and will be gracious to whom I will be gracious, and will show mercy to whom I will show mercy." (Ex. 33:19) That is rightly said of course, but it should be understood that God's free will is not an *arbitrary* will. God had His reasons for doing what He did, but He does not have to give an account of what He is doing. The story respects this, by leaving the reasons obscure.

The story implies that, despite sin, it is still possible to live a life acceptable to God, though it does not state explicitly what constitutes that acceptable life that Abel lived. It also implies that man's life is not *automatically* acceptable to God, though the story does not state explicitly in what respect Cain was unacceptable. It simply points out the two possibilities facing man. We come back to this problem later.

The story does not tell either how Cain knew that God had rejected his offering and had accepted Abel's. It merely states that he knew and thus it sets the scene for the drama that develops.

Cain is very jealous of his brother. A deep anger grows in him. The story states: "his countenance fell," to indicate how deep the event affected him. God does not leave Cain alone in his anger but warns him. He asks: "Why are you angry and why is your countenance fallen?" He continues: "If you do well, you will be accepted" (or, as some translators put it: "you can lift up your countenance"). And then comes the warning: "And if not, sin crouches at the door, its desire is to you, but you must master it." (R.S.V.)

The first part of God's discourse with Cain is not quite clear but it certainly indicates that Cain's rejection is not an ultimate one. For him, too, there is acceptance if he does well. But if not, sin is waiting for an opportunity to attack him and to make him its victim. Cain is left with the decision, he is held responsible. He *can* sin, but he is *not forced* to sin, God invites him to *master* sin.

The warning goes unheeded. Cain talks to Abel. Many ancient manuscripts add here that Cain said: "Let us go out to the field." They go out to the field and there Cain murders Abel. The story seems to hint that Cain hid the body. But God knows.

Just as God came to Adam and Eve, to confront them with their sin, so God comes to Cain to ask an account of what he has done. He asks Cain: "Where is Abel, your brother?" and thereby gives Cain an opportunity to confess and to repent. But

Cain answers willfully: "Am I the shepherd's keeper?" God continues the interrogation: "What have you done?" Another opportunity is opened up to confess. God does not need Cain's confession for His own sake, for He knows what happened. As the story puts it, the blood of Abel shed upon the ground cried to God and this appeal went straightforwardly to God's throne. Cain's confession is needed for Cain's sake.

And then God opens Cain's eyes for the enormity of his crime. He has done something much worse than mere disobedience. He has shed blood that belonged to God and has taken a life that was God's gift and property. And God comes to avenge Abel's innocent blood shed by Cain.

The punishment is severe. Cain is banished from the ground that he tilled. The ground, that drank Abel's blood, will from now on not yield him its fruit. He is doomed to a life of wandering over a hostile earth. Still, even this severe punishment could be a cause for repentance. But instead of breaking down under his guilt, Cain breaks down under his punishment. He answers God: "My punishment is greater than I can bear."

Cain is frightened by the severity of the punishment. To be banished from the tillable ground means for him to be banished from God's presence. He is doomed to a life of wandering without rest and, what is worse, to a life without God's protection. Cain is afraid that anybody might do to *him* what *he* did to Abel, that anybody that finds him might slay him.

Here the story reaches a new climax. Cain learns that he still stands under God's protection. God has punished him severely but has not taken His protection away from Cain. As an indication of this, God puts a mark upon Cain. It is apparently a visible mark; everybody that sees it will know: "this

man is protected by God." And the Lord promises Cain that
He will take vengeance sevenfold on anybody who slays him.
Just as any life, even Cain's life, belongs to God and stands
under God's protection, so vengeance belongs to God, is God's
prerogative.

And then Cain leaves, wandering away from the tillable
land, far away from God and yet protected by God. It would be
vain to ask where he went. "Nod" means "wandering," indicating that Cain does not go to any particular place but embarks
upon a life of wandering and restlessness, presumably in desert
country.

———————

The story runs its course with amazing speed. It hastens to
the climax: Cain's murder of Abel. With this tremendous speed
it seems to convey the idea: "Hardly was there an opportunity,
hardly had Cain and Abel grown up, or Cain killed Abel."
Not only does man's sinful nature go to man's very beginning,
as Gen. 3 states; Gen. 4:1-16 goes far beyond it, in that it
indicates that *man's murderous nature* goes to man's very
beginning.

Gen. 4 tells how sin *spreads*. Adam's sin was not the end
point of the development, it was only the beginning. Disobedience is followed by murder, and murder is followed by something worse, as Gen. 4:17-24 indicates.

The story does not ascribe the murder to the more common motives for murder: possession of goods, of land, of
money, of women. In that respect it differs from the story told
in the "Books of Adam and Eve" mentioned before. These books
ascribe the murder to Cain's desire to marry the sister that his
parents had destined for Abel!

Instead, the story tells that the murder had its starting point at the place where Cain directs himself toward God: at the altar. It is thus not Cain's *worst* side that led to his downfall, but it was his best side: his religious life!

When Adam and Eve were punished, they were driven from the garden, driven from God's nearness. Nevertheless, even outside the garden, where they are sent to till the ground, God is present and acts on their behalf. Cain's punishment results in a further estrangement. He is driven from the tilled ground, and that means for him that he lives where Jahweh is not worshipped: Cain goes "out from the presence of the Lord" as the story puts it.

But even there he is not wholly without God: God continues to protect him. Man's murderous nature, that has shown itself in Cain, should not spread indefinitely. Therefore, God keeps Cain under His protection and thus keeps man's murderous nature in check.

Many interpreters have pointed out that the figure of Cain shows connection with the tribe of the Kenites and that he can be considered as their Patriarch[1]. They worshipped Jahweh and lived mainly a nomadic life outside the region of cultivated land in the near desert. For the Israelites it must have seemed strange that these worshippers of Jahweh lived outside the blessed region of the cultivated land and were yet under Jahweh's protection. The story of Cain and Abel is then supposed to give the reason for this.

All this may be true. Nevertheless, in its present form the story has nothing to do any more with this particular tribe but brings a very particular message: the spreading of human sin and God's response to it.

History is not only a story of disobedience and murder.

God does not leave man alone but continues to act on man's behalf. He warns him against sin, rebukes and punishes him when he has sinned and continues to protect man despite his sin. By doing so, history becomes the story of God's grace. We will see more of this at the end of Gen. 4.

2b. Cain's descendants (Gen. 4:17-24)

The story continues with a list of Cain's descendants followed over eight generations. As mentioned before, this story comes from a different source. Cain is here not a restless wanderer but the builder of the first town, named after his firstborn son, Enoch. The line goes via Enoch, Irad, Mehujael, Methusael and Lamech.

The sons of Lamech are especially mentioned: Jabal, the father of all tent dwellers and cattle raisers, Jubal, the father of musicians, and Tubalcain, the father of artificers in brass and iron. Civilization is taking its course.

It is significant that the building of the first town and the introduction of animal husbandry, arts and crafts are here attributed to the descendants of Cain and not to the descendants of Seth. This does not mean that the author considers civilization bad in itself. Whether civilization is good or bad depends on what is *done* with it. But the story definitely sees culture and civilization in a double light: they *can* be another vehicle of man's willfullness and pride.

In some Israelitic circles, e.g. among the Rechabites, all adaption to (Canaanitic) city life was considered sinful. Also, a critical attitude to many forms of civilization was prevalent in some circles, even in much later ages. For example, the apocryphal book of Enoch pictures arts and crafts as being taught to man by fallen angels.

Originally, the story may have referred to a list of Kenite patriarchs and to Kenite civilization. Kenite towns are known elsewhere in the Bible (1 Sam. 30:29)[1]. Also the Kenites are known as nomadic people, practicing arts and crafts; they were, for example, blacksmiths and musicians.

The main reason for telling the story, however, is a different one. By connecting it with Gen. 4:1-16, it demonstrates how sin is growing and spreading. That is already hinted at by some of the names of Cain's descendants. For example, "Mehujael" means "destroyed by God." The name Methusael, however, has a much better sound, it means "man of God." That is, there is no reason why Cain's descendants should be automatically outside of God's favor. For them, too, there is the possibility to be honored by the name "man of God."[3]

The dark side of the picture predominates, however, as is made clear by Lamech's famous "sword song." Here the wildness and bloodthirstyness is exaggerated to the extreme. A man wounded Lamech, hence he was killed. A young man hurt Lamech, hence, he was killed too.

In the story of Cain and Abel, vengeance belonged to God. *God* would avenge Cain seven times, but Cain should not avenge himself. But Lamech takes vengeance in his own hands and this vengeance is much stronger than anything that God promised to Cain; not seven times, but seventy-seven times! God's promise to Cain emphasizes that human life is sacred and under God's protection. Lamech's sword song emphasizes that human life is cheap and that he will take somebody's life almost without provocation.

This is *one* possible end point of human history. It goes from disobedience via murder to a chaotic existence where the hand of everyone is against everybody else. Is that how human history *must* end? That this is not the case can be seen from the other list of Adam's descendants.

2c. The genealogy from Adam to Noah (Gen. 4:25-26, 5:29)

This genealogy starts with Adam and goes via Seth to Noah. As mentioned before, only the beginning and the end of the genealogy list of J has been preserved, the larger middle part has been replaced by the genealogy list of P.

The name "Adam" is here used as a *personal* name, not as a general name. He is the patriarch of a long list of descendants. The name "Seth" is described as meaning "appointed": he is appointed as the replacement for Abel, whom Cain slew. This connects J's genealogy list with Gen. 4:1-16. The name "Enos" means man. He teaches man to call upon the name of Jahweh. The main Old Testament tradition (Ex. 3:14, 6:3) dates the worship of Jahweh back to the time of Moses. According to J, however, Jahweh was worshipped at all times even back into the early history. It is difficult to decide whether this means that Jahweh was *actually* worshipped in the very early days or whether J merely claims that Jahweh was *factually* worshipped in the early worship acts.

A true man according to the Bible is a man who prays. He does not trust in his own power and strength, but calls upon the strength that the Lord can provide. He does not take his life in his *own hand* but puts his life into *God's hand.*

To "call upon the name of the Lord" presupposes knowledge of God. For the expression: "the name of the Lord" means "God as He revealed Himself." To know the name of the Lord means to know His power, His glory and His grace. According to J, man knew about this from the very beginning. Man thus can have this knowledge of the Lord and worship Him accordingly. His road does not necessarily end where Lamech's road ended.

The same idea is expressed in the saying about Noah. It tells of men deeply bent under the weight of their guilt and expecting with fervent hope their salvation from the harsh conditions under which they live.

What is the comfort that Noah is expected to bring? Some interpreters have pointed out that Noah planted a vineyard and that wine can make man forget his troubles. Vineyards were indeed highly treasured in Israel. To possess one and to use its fruit was the longing of every Israelite. But wine is not always a blessing, as Noah's drunkenness shows, so that this interpretation may not be correct.

Others have pointed to Noah's offering after the flood, mentioned in Gen. 8 as part of J's flood account. According to J's flood story this offering reconciled God and man. This seems to come closer to the truth.

What then is the life that is acceptable to God? It is a life in which man does not expect anything from himself but where he expects everything from God. It is a life bent under sin but expecting God's salvation. It is a life of prayer, a life reconciled with God through an offering acceptable to God. In other words, it is a life of *faith*.

We can now answer the question why Abel's offering was accepted. It is as the Letter to the Hebrews states: "By faith Abel offered unto God a more excellent sacrifice than Cain" (Hebr. 1:4a). The secret of Abel's life was *faith*, the secret of Cain's life was *unbelief*[2].

This section belongs to the second part of Gen. 4 by sheer contrast. Gen. 4 shows two possible ways of human life: Cain's way and Seth's way. And it leaves it up to the listeners to make the choice.

REFERENCES:

[1]Gerhard von Rad, see Chapter 3.

[2]Alan Richardson, see Chapter 3.

[3]Hellmuth Frey, see Chapter 3.

CHAPTER SEVEN

Adam's Genealogy According to P

1. The Text. Gen. 5 minus 5:29.

(1) This is the book of the generations of Adam. In the day that God created man, in the likeness of God made he him; (2) Male and female created he them; and blessed them, and called their name Adam, in the day when they were created.

(3) And Adam lived an hundred and thirty years, and begat a son in his own likeness, after his image; and called his name Seth: (4) And the days of Adam after he had begotten Seth were eight hundred years: and he begat sons and daughters: (5) And all the days that Adam lived were nine hundred and thirty years: and he died.

(6) And Seth lived an hundred and five years, and begat Enos: (7) And Seth lived after he begat Enos eight hundred and seven years, and begat sons and daughters: (8) And all the days of Seth were nine hundred and twelve years: and he died.

(9) And Enos lived ninety years, and begat Cainan: (10) And Enos lived after he begat Cainan eight hundred and fifteen years, and begat sons and daughters: (11) And all the days of Enos were nine hundred and five years: and he died.

(12) And Cainan lived seventy years, and begat Mahalaleel: (13) And Cainan lived after he begat Mahalaleel eight hundred and forty years, and begat sons and daughters: (14) And all the days of Cainan were nine hundred and ten years: and he died.

(15) And Mahalaleel lived sixty and five years, and begat Jared: (16) And Mahalaleel lived after he begat Jared eight hundred and thirty years, and begat sons and daughters: (17) And all the days of Mahalaleel were eight hundred ninety and five years: and he died.

(18) And Jared lived an hundred sixty and two years, and he begat Enoch: (19) And Jared lived after he begat Enoch eight hundred years, and begat sons and daughters: (20) And all the days of Jared were nine hundred sixty and two years: and he died.

(21) And Enoch lived sixty and five years, and begat Methuselah: (22) And Enoch walked with God after he begat Methuselah three hundred years, and begat sons and daughters: (23) And all the days of Enoch were three hundred sixty and five years: (24) And Enoch walked with God: and he was not; for God took him.

(25) And Methuselah lived an hundred eighty and seven years, and begat Lamech. (26) And Methuselah lived after he begat Lamech seven hundred eighty and two years, and begat sons and daughters: (27) And all the days of Methuselah were nine hundred sixty and nine years: and he died.

(28) And Lamech lived an hundred eighty and two years, and begat a son (Noah): (30) And Lamech lived after he begat Noah five hundred ninety and five years, and begat sons and daughters: (31) And all the days of Lamech were seven hundred seventy and seven years: and he died.

(32) And Noah was five hundred years old: and Noah begat Shem, Ham, and Japheth.

(The word between brackets was added for clarification. Gen. 5:29 belongs to J.)

2. Discussion.

This list of Adam's genealogy, going from Adam to Noah, belongs to P. The seemingly dead list of names should not be considered as being without theological significance. On the contrary, it too is sacred teaching of the priests and should be accepted as such. Even a list of names plus a few data contains a message.

Long lists of descendants of patriarchs are common to many religions. According to James Michener's book *Hawaii* the Hawaiian natives had long lists of kings going back to before the settlement of Hawaii by natives from Bora-Bora. The Babylonians had long lists of kings, including a series of kings dating from before the flood.

That list of names of Babylonian kings shows many resemblances with the list given in Gen. 5. Both contain ten names. The name of the third man, when translated, means "man" in both lists. In both lists the seventh was taken up into heaven. In both lists the tenth was the hero of the ark that escaped from the flood[1, 3].

In addition, these kings had an extremely long life; ages of 25,000-30,000 years are common. There seems to be a fixed ratio between the ages of the members of the two genealogies and a similar ratio between the ages at which the first son was born. It would go too far, however, to assume outright interdependence as was done during the last century.

There are important differences of course. The Babylonian list is a list of kings. P's list contains the names of ordinary men. Or perhaps, not so ordinary men, for they are "the holy man of old," the line of "believers[2]."

People have often wondered about the longevity of these patriarchs. But when one compares their ages with those of the Babylonian genealogy, it is perhaps even more surprising that their lives were so short. On the average they are about 30 times shorter than the Babylonian lifetimes, against only about 12 times longer than our lifetimes! What does this signify?

The long lifetimes of the Babylonian genealogy probably are a consequence of the idea: "How strong must our forefathers have been that the whole human race could have descended from them! They must have been superhuman!" The relatively "short" lifetimes of Gen. 5 can possibly be seen as a reaction to this: "Our forefathers were strong, but they were not *that* strong. They were not superhuman, they were human. They were creatures, they were sinners." This could then be seen as the equivalent of J's story of man's fall.

The ages in Gen. 5 have been worked over several times[1]. In the Codex A Methuselah lived until fourteen years after the flood. According to the Samaritan text Methuselah lived for a mere 720 years. Codex D and the King James text let Methuselah die in the year of the flood. It is probable that these ages contain a message, but some of the keys to the message are missing. When it is said that Enoch lived for 365 years, that is as many years as there are days in the year, then this might indicate that Enoch lived a full life in the author's view.

Comparing Gen. 5 with the other Genesis genealogies, it is seen that the lifetimes shorten as time goes on. From Adam to Noah it is 700-1000 years, from Noah to Abraham 200-600 years, for the patriarchs it is 100-200 years and later it is 70-80 years. This is often considered as suggesting that man's life-time shortens when sin spreads. J states something similar in Gen. 6, indicating that J and P agree on this point.

The section starts with the creation of Adam. Von Rad[1] suggests that the word "Adam" in Gen. 5:2 should be read "man." That God calls their name "man" indicates that God establishes their proper place in the realm of creation and that God establishes His rule over them. From here on "Adam" is a *personal* name, not a general name as in Gen. 2. He is the first patriarch of a long list of holy men of old.

It is again stated that Adam was made in the likeness of God. Adam's son is in Adam's likeness and after his image. Some theologians have suggested that the latter conveys the idea that Seth was a sinner like Adam was. Von Rad[1], and many other Old Testament scholars with him, maintains that it means that Seth was also made in the image of God. That fits with the use of the expression "image of God" in Gen. 9.

The list has an almost monotonous sequence of events: birth-parenthood-death. These are the basic events of human existence. These events are thereby seen as part of God's plan concerning sinful man.

The text makes a more detailed statement about Enoch. "Enoch walked with God" says the text. The only other one about whom this is said is Noah. All great believers after the flood walk at best "before God," but not "with God." This hints at an extremely close relationship between Enoch and God.

After having said something about Enoch's age, the text concludes: "and he was not, for God took him." The term "to take" is used in the sense of "to take up into heaven." It is interesting to see how in a few simple words an important message is presented. In the sequence of people who were born, lived and died, there was *one* who broke the general rule: "Enoch." He was born, lived and was taken up into heaven. Why? Because he "walked with God" says the text. God chooses freely, but His choice is not arbitrary. And God has power, even over death. That is what the passage about Enoch tries to convey.

Because of the high ages of Adam's descendants there are peculiar synchronisms: Adam saw the birth of Lamech, Seth lived after Enoch was taken up into heaven, Noah died when Abraham was 60 years old and Shem was still alive when Esau and Jacob were born. Luther was quite fascinated by the idea that so many generations of holy men of old were contemporaries and knew each other. Since everything in P is well calculated and well thought through, one can be quite certain that the list of ages was also given purposely.

Does this mean that men in ancient times actually grew that old? Not necessarily; the long ages were stated purposely to get a particular message across. Some of the details of that message escape us at present. It would thus be futile either to verify these ages or to search for physiological reasons why people could have grown that old in the past.

What then does the genealogy list of Gen. 5, and the other genealogy lists following it, aim at? They probably aim at getting a variety of ideas across. One that should concern us perhaps the most is that they lay the connection between creation and Israel. The line of the genealogy goes from Adam, via Noah and Abraham to the historical existence of Israel as a nation. The stories of creation and fall do not stand isolated at the beginning of time, but are thus connected with Israel's own history. One of the reasons for the genealogy lists, though not the only one, is to make this connection. *That alone* already classifies it as sacred teaching.

REFERENCES:

[1]Gerhard von Rad, see Chapter 3.
[2]Alan Richardson, see Chapter 3.
[3]Hellmuth Frey, see Chapter 3.

CHAPTER EIGHT

The Two Accounts of the Flood
In Genesis 6-8

1. Introduction.

If one reads the Genesis account of the flood carefully, one is struck by the large number of repetitions. There are also discrepancies in the duration of the flood. One section gives 40 days of rain and 21 days for drying up and the other gives 150 days of rain and about 200 days for drying up.

These repetitions and discrepancies come about because the flood account is actually a blend of two stories, one belonging to J, the other to P. The stories can easily be separated and then put together as two complete stories, thereby leaving only the position of very few sentences in any doubt*. When this has been completed, each story is self-consistent; both the repetitions and the discrepancies have disappeared.

For a good understanding of the flood account both stories should be discussed separately. For though they agree as far as the main events and the interpretation of these events are concerned, they differ in details. And it is in these details that the fine points of the two messages are found.

---

*One might e.g. question the exact position of Gen. 7:16b: "and the Lord shut him in," belonging to the J-account.

After this has been done, it should be taken into account that the two stories were joined together *purposely* in an editorial process. And that means that one must ultimately emphasize what the two stories *have in common*. This gives an opportunity to deal with the problem of discrepancies in the Biblical account[3].

Then it should be considered that the two stories show remarkable similarities with Babylonian flood accounts as far as the *facts* are concerned. It should not be forgotten, however, that the two types of account differ strongly in the *interpretation* of those facts. Most theologians no longer hold to the idea of a *direct* dependence of the Biblical and the Babylonian flood stories, though their relationship is not denied[2].

Finally one has to deal with archaeological and historical confirmations of the flood, since they shed an interesting light on the background of the Babylonian and Biblical flood stories. The attempts to demonstrate that the flood was a *universal* flood spreading over the whole earth, and not a *local* flood covering major parts of the Euphrates-Tigris valley, are not in the same category. They can only be discussed adequately in the scientific part of this book.

2. The flood story according to J.

2a. The Text (see G. von Rad[1]).

6:1-4. (1) And it came to pass, when men began to multiply on the face of the earth, and daughters were born unto them, (2) That the sons of God saw the daughters of man that they were fair; and they took them wives of all which they chose. (3) And the Lord said, My Spirit shall not always strive with man, for that he also is flesh: yet his days shall be an hundred and twenty years. (4) There were giants in the earth in those days; and also after that, when the sons of God come in unto the daughters of man, and they bare children to them, the same became mighty men which were of old, men of renown.

6:5-8. (5) And God saw that the wickedness of man was great in the earth, and that every imagination of the thoughts of his heart was only evil continually. (6) And it repented the Lord that he had made man on the earth, and it grieved him at his heart. (7) And the Lord said, I will destroy man whom I have created from the face of the earth; both man, and beast, and the creeping thing, and the fowls of the air; for it repenteth me that I have made them. (8) But Noah found grace in the eyes of the Lord.

7:1-5. (1) And the Lord said unto Noah, Come thou and all thy house into the ark; for thee have I seen righteous before me in this generation. (2) Of every clean beast thou shalt take to thee by sevens, the male and his female: and of beasts that are not clean by two, the male and his female. (3) Of fowls also of the air by sevens, the male and the female; to keep seed alive upon the face of all the earth. (4) For yet seven days, and I will cause it to rain upon the earth forty days and forty nights; and every living substance that I have made will I destroy from off the face of the earth. (5) And Noah did according unto all that the Lord commanded him.

7:7, 16b, 8-10. (7) And Noah went in, and his sons, and his wife, and his sons' wives with him, into the ark, because of the waters of the flood. (16b) And the Lord shut him in. (8) Of clean beasts, and of beasts that are not clean, and of fowls, and of every thing that creepeth upon the earth, (9) There went in two and two unto Noah into the ark, the male and the female, as God had commanded Noah. (10) And it came to pass after seven days, that the waters of the flood were upon the earth.

7:12, 17b, 22-23. *(12) And the rain was upon the earth forty days and forty nights. (17b) And the waters increased, and bare up the ark, and it was lift up above the earth. (22) All in whose nostrils was the breath of life, of all that was in the dry land, died. (23) And every living substance was destroyed which was upon the face of the ground, both man, and cattle, and the creeping things, and the fowl of the heaven; and they were destroyed from the earth: and Noah only remained alive, and they that were with him in the ark.*

Gen. 8:6a, 2b, 3a, 6b, 8-12, 13b. *(6a) And it came to pass at the end of forty days, (2b) (that) the rain from heaven was restrained. (3a) And the waters returned from off the earth continually: (6b) (And) Noah opened the window of the ark which he had made: (8) (and) he sent forth a dove from him, to see if the waters were abated from off the face of the ground; (9) But the dove found no rest for the sole of her foot, and she returned unto him into the ark, for the waters were on the face of the whole earth: then he put forth his hands, and took her, and pulled her in unto him into the ark. (10) And he stayed yet other seven days; and again he sent forth the dove out of the ark; (11) And the dove came in to him in the evening; and lo, in her mouth was an olive leaf pluckt off: so Noah knew that the waters were abated from off the earth. (12) And he stayed yet other seven days; and sent forth the dove; which returned not again unto him any more. (13b) And Noah removed the covering of the ark, and looked, and, behold, the face of the ground was dry.*

8:20-22. *(20) And Noah builded an altar unto the Lord; and took of every clean beast, and of every clean fowl, and offered burnt offerings on the altar. (21) And the Lord smelled a sweet savour; and the Lord said in his heart, I will not again curse the ground any more for man's sake; for the imagination of man's heart is evil from his youth; neither will I again smite any more every thing living, as I have done. (22) While the earth remaineth, seedtime and harvest, and cold and heat, and summer and winter, and day and night shall not cease.*

(The words between parentheses were changed to conform with von Rad's version.)

2b. Discussion.

In ancient mythologies one reads about gods marrying women and producing offspring. Their children are the great heroes, the men of great fame. These stories interpret the existence of these heroes and these men of fame in terms of their divine origin. They form the high points of human development, made possible by divine intervention.

It seems at first that the Biblical writer of Gen. 6:1-4 has taken over this idea completely. For the term "sons of God" should be understood as "heavenly beings." Some interpreters have suggested that the "daughters of man" are the descendants of Cain and the "sons of God" are the descendants of Seth, but that goes completely against the clear meaning of the text.

It would mean a wrong judgment on our part, however, if this section were seen as a return to ancient mythology. If one follows the four-tradition theory, this section belongs to L, together with the story of the tower of Babel. It has a strongly polemic ring, almost amounting to sarcasm. In that manner the references to mythology become part of an effort to *demythologize* the world.

True enough, the writer tells without restraint of the marriage between heavenly beings and the daughters of man and of their heroic, gigantic, famous offspring. But far from being hailed as the high point of human development, they are instead seen as a calamity. The mixing of heavenly powers with humans makes not only heroism and fame increase, but it also makes *sin* increase without bounds. The author thus sees a result that is a complete parody of what the ancient mythologies aim at.

God answers this calamity by the verdict "My spirit shall not always strive with man, for that he is also flesh: yet his days shall be an hundred and twenty years." God limits the titanic efforts of mankind and the outpouring of man's sin by limiting man's life span.

The scene is now set for the great drama of the flood. The text (Gen. 6:5-8) sees in man an accumulation of wickedness. It does not merely state that man makes a few mistakes here and there, but instead it maintains that "every imagination and every thought of man's heart is only evil continually." There is *nothing* in man that is good in God's sight. This goes much further than stating that man is a sinner; it emphasizes that man is a sinner *only*. The doctrine of man's "depravity" finds here its classical expression.

And then the writer pictures what this does to God by giving his readers and listeners a look into God's heart[1]. He is not afraid of using bold anthropomorphisms in his exposition. And, as von Rad points out, he does not rely on earlier tradition but speaks for himself. To him God is not an abstract idea throning far above earthly things, but a person, a living will, who is intimately involved in and concerned with all that goes on on earth. For that reason the author can say that the Lord is *grieved* by man's sinful condition and that He *repents* of having created man.

God makes the decision to destroy man and all living creatures with him. The author does not picture a "vengeful" God, but a God who suffers when sin is committed. The destruction of man, which brings the destruction of all living creatures with it, is not done in a fit of anger but is part of God's plan to *restore* His creation to its original purpose. The destruction is not a punishment, but the prelude to this restauration.

For *one* man is excluded from the general destruction. Only *one* man can be found who can be used in God's plan: Noah. Not that Noah was not also a sinner. He was not chosen for merit but for serviceability. The idea was not that Noah could lay claims that he *deserved* to be spared and *deserved* to be used. As the author puts it: "Noah found grace in the eyes of the Lord." Hence, it was God's grace to choose him and to use him, it was not Noah's merit.

What does the word "righteous" mean? It does not mean "sinless." In the Old Testament somebody is called righteous if he responds adequately to the relationship in which he is placed[1]. When God acts in accordance with His covenant with man, God is called "righteous"; that is, He is gracious to man. If a man stands in the right relationship to God, that is, if he believes and trusts God, then he is "righteous," even though he is a sinner. The term "righteous" is a theological evaluation of this relationship and not a juristic one.

The command to build the ark is missing from the story. Apparently the editor who joined the flood stories of J and P together thought that P's extensive discussion covered the subject adequately. There is no doubt, however, that such a command was part of the original story, since Gen. 7:1-5 tells of

God's command to *enter* the *finished* ark. It is therefore logical that there must have been a command to *build* the ark in the first place.

The story implies that Noah did not know *why* he built the ark. Noah obeyed God's command blindly without asking "why." Only after the ark has been completed, God tells him of the impending destruction of all creation by a flood and of God's plan to save Noah and his household. In other words, God tested Noah and Noah passed the test. Noah responded adequately to the situation and hence he is called righteous.

God not only cares for Noah and his household, He also cares for the survival of all living creatures. They should be taken into the ark, one pair of each, but the clean beasts and fowl should be taken by sevens. The reason is that some of them will be used for sacrifices after the flood.

Noah does all that God commanded him. After everything has been completed, and Noah, his house, and the animals have gone into the ark, "the Lord closes the door behind him." Apparently there are no windows in the ark, only an opening in the roof. Noah, his house and the animals sit in the ark, unknowing what will happen on the earth. But they are safe, for God has them under His protection and care, though destruction will visit the earth.

And then the flood comes. Forty days and forty nights* the rain falls down upon the earth. The waters increase, cover the land and bear up the ark. All living creatures drown, only Noah and those that are with him in the ark remain alive.

---

*The term "forty days and forty nights" is a standard Biblical expression that should not be taken too literally. Moses stayed forty days and forty nights on Mount Sinai. Elijah walked forty days and forty nights through the wilderness to Mount Horeb. Jesus stayed forty days and forty nights in the wilderness to be tempted by the devil.

After forty days the rain stops and the waters recede. Noah cannot look out over the submerged earth and has to rely on other methods of reconnaissance. After seven days he opens the window in the roof and lets out a dove. But the dove does not find a place of rest; it returns and Noah takes it back into the ark. After seven more days Noah tries again. This time the dove comes back in the evening with a fresh olive leaf in its mouth. Apparently there is fresh life and there are opportunities for the dove to rest, but no opportunities to stay out permanently. After another seven days Noah tries for the third time and this time the dove does not return. Noah sees this as a sign that the waters have receded from the earth. Hence he removes the top of the ark and sees that the ground is dry.

The story is told in a simple fashion. There is nothing spectacular here. In sober words the calamity is described, but perhaps just because of it the story heightens its impact.

There is no mention of high mountains over which the ark first floats and later comes to rest. All events seem to occur in relatively low-lying country. This is in stark contrast with P's flood account.

After Noah and his household come out of the ark, he first builds an altar unto the Lord to sacrifice upon it of every clean beast and every clean fowl. It is a burnt offering offered to God, aiming at reconciling God and man. In the offering the righteous Noah confesses that man deserves punishment and death, but he appeals to God to accept in his stead the death of the animal that is offered. This shows that Noah was indeed "righteous," that he stood in the right relationship to God.

God accepts Noah's offering. With a characteristic anthropomorphism the author states: "And the Lord smelled a sweet savour; and the Lord said in his heart, I will not again curse the ground any more for man's sake." According to J, therefore, the curse of the ground is lifted after the flood. That was why Noah's father said hopefully at Noah's birth: "This same shall comfort us concerning our work and the toil of our hands, because of the ground which the Lord hath cursed." This hope is now fulfilled.

The lifting of the curse is accompanied by the argumentation: "for the imagination of man's heart is evil from his youth." Does this mean that God has now resigned Himself to man's sinfulness? No, it means that God has decided to give *undeserved* grace instead of *deserved* punishment. For that reason God promises: "neither will I smite any more every thing living as I have done."

The story ends with the solemn promise: "While the earth remaineth, seedtime and harvest, and cold and heat, and summer and winter, and day and night shall not cease." The author thus sees the life of the Palestine farmer as being guaranteed by God's promise.

The story of the flood, as given by J, is not only a story of human sin and of God's wrath over sin; it is also and above all a story of God's grace. Stronger than God's wrath over sin is God's desire for man's salvation.

This does not mean that God's wrath over sin is glossed over. On the contrary, it is emphasized to stress the enormity of man's sin. It forms the grim background against which the acts of God's grace are placed so that the miracle of this grace is better recognized.

As the flood story puts it, life on earth had to be brought to the brink of total destruction before God and man became reconciled. According to the New Testament, the only begotten Son of God had to give His life to bring salvation and grace to mankind. Both illustrate Bonhoeffer's favored expression[6]: "Grace is not *cheap* grace, it is expensive grace.

3. The flood story according to P.

3a. The Text (see G. von Rad[1]).

6:9-22. *(9) These are the generations of Noah: Noah was a just man and perfect in his generations, and Noah walked with God. (10) And Noah begat three sons, Shem, Ham, and Japheth. (11) The earth also was corrupt before God, and the earth was filled with violence. (12) And God looked upon the earth, and, behold, it was corrupt; for all flesh had corrupted his way upon the earth. (13) And God said unto Noah, The end of all flesh is come before me; for the earth is filled with violence through them; and behold, I will destroy them with the earth. (14) Make thee an ark of gopher wood; rooms shalt thou make in the ark, and shalt pitch it within and without with pitch. (15) And this is the fashion which thou shalt make it of: The length of the ark shall be three hundred cubits, the breadth of it fifty cubits, and the height of it thirty cubits. (16) A window shalt thou make to the ark, and in a cubit shalt thou finish it above; and the door of the ark shalt thou set in the side thereof; with lower, second, and third stories shalt thou make it. (17) And, behold, I, even I, do bring a flood of waters upon the earth, to destroy all flesh, wherein is the breath of life, from under heaven; and everything that is in the earth shall die. (18) But with thee will I establish my covenant; and thou shalt come into the ark, thou, and thy sons, and thy wife, and thy son's wives with thee. (19) And of every living thing of all flesh, two of every sort shalt thou bring into the ark, to keep them alive with thee; they shall be male and female. (20) Of fowls after their kind, and of cattle after their kind, of every creeping thing of the earth after his kind, two of every sort shall come unto thee, to keep them alive. (21) And take thou unto thee of all food that is eaten, and thou shalt gather it to thee; and it shall be for food for thee, and for them. (22) Thus did Noah according to all that God commanded him, so did he.*

7:6, 11, 13-16a. *(6) And Noah was six hundred years old when the flood of waters was upon the earth. (11) In the six hundredth year of Noah's life, in the second month, the seventeenth day of the month, the same day were all the fountains of the great deep broken up, and the windows of heaven were opened. (13) In the selfsame day entered Noah, and Shem, and Ham, and Japheth, the sons of Noah, and Noah's wife, and the three wives of his sons with them, into the ark; (14) They, and every beast after his kind, and all the cattle after their kind, and every creeping thing that creepeth upon the earth after his kind, and every fowl after his kind, every bird of every sort. (15) And they went in unto Noah into the ark, two and two of all flesh, wherein is the breath of life. (16a) And they that went in, went in male and female of all flesh, as God had commanded him.*

7:17a, 18-21, 24. *(17a) (Thus the flood came upon the earth). (18) And the waters prevailed, and were increased greatly upon the earth; and the ark went upon the face of the waters. (19) And the waters prevailed exceedingly upon the earth; and all the high hills, that were under the whole heaven, were covered. (20) Fifteen cubits upward did the waters prevail; and the mountains were covered. (21) And all flesh died that moved upon the earth, both of fowl, and of cattle, and of beast, and of every creeping thing that creepeth upon the earth, and every man: (24) And the waters prevailed upon the earth an hundred and fifty days.*

8:1-2a, 3b-5, 7, 13a, 14. (1) And God remembered Noah, and every living thing, and all the cattle that was with him in the ark: and God made a wind to pass over the earth, and the waters assuaged; (2a) The fountains also of the deep and the windows of heaven were stopped. (3b) And after the end of the hundred and fifty days the waters were abated. (4) And the ark rested in the seventh month, on the seventeenth day of the month, upon the mountains of Ararat. (5) And the waters decreased continually until the tenth month: in the tenth month, on the first day of the month, were the tops of the mountains seen. (7) And he sent forth a raven, which went forth to and fro, until the waters were dried up from off the the earth. (13a) And it came to pass in the six hundredth and first year, in the first month, the first day of the month, the waters were dried up from off the earth: (14) And in the second month, on the seven and twentieth day of the month, was the earth dried.

Gen. 8:15-19. (15) And God spake unto Noah, saying, (16) Go forth of the ark, thou, and thy wife, and thy sons, and thy sons' wives with thee. (17) Bring forth with thee every living thing that is with thee, of all flesh, both of fowl, and of cattle, and of every creeping thing that creepeth upon the earth; that they may breed abundantly in the earth, and be fruitful, and multiply upon the earth. (18) And Noah went forth, and his sons, and his wife, and his sons' wives with him: (19) Every beast, every creeping thing, and every fowl, and whatsoever creepeth upon the earth, after their kinds, went forth out of the ark.

(Note: In Gen. 7:17a the version of von Rad is used.)

3b. Discussion.

As mentioned before, P's account is part of a "book of

generations." It starts with creation ("the generations of the heavens and the earth"), continues with the genealogy of Adam ("the book of generations of Adam") and then proceeds with the flood. Characteristically the story begins "These are the generations of Noah."

The author says about Noah: "Noah was a just man and perfect in his generations." The expressions "just" and "perfect" do not mean "perfect" in the absolute or moral sense. It is a concept of the sacred priestly language and refers to a man who has been justified by the cult and has thus been put into a state with which God is well pleased.

The author continues: "Noah walked with God." This expresses the existence of a very close relationship. The only other man of which this is said in the Bible is Enoch.

The P-version of Genesis does not have a story of man's fall. That does not mean that the *fact* of man's fall, that is man's sinfulness, was unknown to P. On the contrary, Gen. 6 speaks of it in no uncertain terms as follows: "The earth also was corrupt before God, and the earth was filled with violence. And God looked upon the earth, and, behold, it was corrupt; for all flesh had corrupted his way upon the earth." P thus characterizes the situation by *one* word, "violence." He sees it as the most serious sin against Jahweh and as a desecration of God's good earth[1]. In this respect P and J are in full agreement.

Noah is told before he builds the ark, what is going to happen to all mankind; this is in contrast to J's version where Noah learns of the reason for building the ark after its completion. God will bring a flood upon the earth that will destroy all living creatures except those that take shelter in the ark. For that reason Noah is told: "The end of all flesh is come before me; for the earth is filled with violence through them; and, behold, I will destroy them *with* the earth. Make thee an ark of gopher wood."

The impending catastrophe is of apocalyptic proportions. In the J-version of the flood God destroys all flesh *from* the earth but leaves the earth itself intact. In the P-version, however, not only all flesh is destroyed, but the earth is destroyed *with* it. The reason for this difference hangs together with P's cosmology, as will be seen in a moment.

Noah receives detailed instructions about how to build the ark. It should be 450 feet long, 75 feet wide and 45 feet deep. It should have a window in the top (as in J) and a door in the side (contrary to J). It should be divided into three stories and should be made watertight. The ark will house Noah and his family and all the animals, two of each kind. Food must be taken in in sufficient quantities to feed both man and beast.

Noah and his family are spared from the general destruction by going into the ark. God makes a covenant with them and promises them to keep them safe.

In P's cosmology, as found in Gen. 1, the waters stored in heaven were separated from the waters on earth and the waters on earth are separated from the dry land. God keeps the cosmic order by keeping this separation intact. But now a flood of great proportions comes over the earth. And that means for P that the old cosmic order is destroyed. Hence, the text states: "In the six hundredth year of Noah's life, in the second month, the seventeenth day of the month, the same day were all the fountains of the great deep broken up, and the windows of heaven were opened." Consequently, P can say that the earth is destroyed *with* all flesh. Note how well the author's cosmology blends with the story he has to tell.

Since the flood is a much greater calamity than in J, it lasts 150 days instead of 40 days, and it takes a much longer time before the waters recede. The whole event lasts more than a year.

Just as the dimensions of the ark are important to the author, so the dates are important to him. It is carefully mentioned when the rain starts, when it stops, how high the waters rose, when the ark rests on the mountains of Ararat, when the tops of the mountains are seen, when the water has disappeared and when the ground is dry.

The waters rise fifteen cubits (22½ feet, half the height of the ark) above the highest mountains. There are two reasons for mentioning this. One is to emphasize that the height of the water is adequate for drowning all living creatures: "And all flesh died that moved upon the earth, both of fowl, and of cattle, and of beast, and of every creeping thing that creepeth upon the earth, and every man." The second reason is to make sure that the ark can just barely float over the highest mountains; as soon as the rain stops, the ark will come to rest there.

Noah and those that are with him in the ark are saved, for "God remembered Noah, and every living thing, and all the cattle that was with him in the ark." Finally it is enough: "the fountains of the deep and the windows of heaven were stopped," says the text. It is interesting to note once more how well the ancient cosmology matches the story.

The waters recede and the ark comes to rest on the mountains of Ararat. Why these Armenian mountains? For a very simple reason: they were the highest mountains known to people in the ancient Middle East and therefore the water had to come so high that *they* were adequately covered. Obviously, when the waters recede, the ark comes to rest on the top of these mountains.

Apparently Noah can look out over the water, for he can see the tops of the mountains reappear. He lets out a raven, which flies back and forth until the waters have dried up. There are already places where the raven can rest but there is apparently no food for him except in the ark.

After the waters have disappeared, Noah does not leave the ark immediately. For the land is not yet safe to walk on, it must dry up completely. The author allows adequate time (two months) for this purpose. Finally God commands Noah to leave the ark and to bring out all the animals.

The animals are blessed and are commanded to "be fruitful, and multiply upon the earth." The blessing, given at the beginning, is thus repeated. The event of the flood could make one doubt whether the original blessing is still valid and for that reason it is necessary to repeat it and thus remove the doubt.

The flood story of P shows God's power and God's freedom. He has power to create this world, He can also let it sink back into chaos. God's wrath over sin is stressed so that His grace can be seen as a miracle of His love. Grace, once again, is not "cheap" grace, it is "expensive" grace.

P sees the flood as a calamity of eschatological proportions that becomes visible in retrospect[1]. Mankind after Noah has no direct relationship any more to the world that, when created, was "very good." That world is separated from us by the eschatological judgment of the flood, according to the text.

4. The flood in archaeology[4, 5].

The two Biblical flood stories show remarkable similarities

with Babylonian flood accounts as far as the *facts* are concerned. They differ widely from the Biblical accounts in the interpretation of these facts.

The earliest account of the flood is the Sumerian one, dating back to at least 2000 B.C. The best preserved text is the Assyrian text of the Gilgamesh epic, dating from the 7th century B.C. A later version in prose, attributed to a priest of the temple of Marduk in Babylon, was written around 275 B.C.

Let us look for a moment at the points of agreement between the Gilgamesh epic and the Biblical flood accounts. The hero of the Gilgamesh epic is Uta-napisjtim (= Uta is my life). The poem has the following highlights[5]:

1. The gods decide to destroy mankind for their sins.
2. The god Ea warns Uta-napisjtim and commands him to build a ship.
3. Animals and all living creatures should be brought into the ship.
4. The flood comes, it lasts six days and seven nights.
5. All mankind returns to clay.
6. The ship rests on the mountains of Nisir in Kurdistan.
7. Uta-napisjtim determines the height of the water by releasing birds (dove, swallow, raven).
8. After the flood Uta-napisjtim brings a sacrifice to the gods.
9. The gods smell the sweet savour.
10. The god Enlil is reconciled with Uta-napisjtim.
11. Enlil blesses Uta-napisjtim and his wife and makes them equal to the gods.

Because of the large areas of agreement as far as the basic facts are concerned, it is not so surprising that a direct dependence between the Babylonian and the Biblical flood accounts was assumed in earlier days. Modern theologians, however, have a better idea about the important differences in the background and in the interpretation of the story. The Gilgamesh epic is very crudely polytheistic, for example.

It is probably safe to assume that all the accounts of the flood, including the Biblical ones, are accounts of the *same* event. They are perhaps based upon a common tradition, but they differ among each other in detail and in interpretation.

As the archaeological record indicates, the flood story was known over most of the Middle East so that it is not surprising that the Israelites were familiar with it. According to one Biblical tradition Abraham came from Ur, so that the flood account could have been preserved orally. In addition, the Canaanites seem to have known a similar story, so that the Israelites could have taken it over if they had not known it before.

There are many additional archaeological verifications of the flood account[5]. Indication of serious flooding have been found in Uruk, the town of Gilgamesh, and in Sjurruppak, the town where the gods gathered together and decided upon the destruction of mankind. This must have occurred around 3000 B.C. Indications of serious flooding in Kisj date from the same period. Flood indications from Nineveh and Ur date from much earlier periods, however. For that reason it is difficult to decide which of these events later became known as *the* flood.

The indications of the flooding are quite spectacular in some cases. Woolley found in Ur a layer of clean, water-laid clay of about 3-4 yards thick. A similar layer found in Uruk was about 5 feet thick and a corresponding layer found in Kisj was about 1 foot thick. This indicates that local floods of very substantial proportions must have occurred.

Other archaeological references to the flood are found on prisms[5]. One prism gives the names of five towns existing before the flood: Eridu, Badtibira, Larak, Sippar and Sjurruppak. The name of the King of Sjurruppak is listed as Ubar-Tutu, which was the father of Uta-napisjtim according to the Gilgamesh epic. It also has the following inscription: "The flood came. After the flood had come, the kingdom descended again from heaven. The kingdom came to Kisj." Another tablet gives the names of Su-kur-lam, the son of Ubar-Tutu and of Ziusudra, the son of Su-kur-lam. Ziusudra is the hero of the Sumerian flood story.

It seems therefore safe to conclude that all the flood stories refer to a *local flood* of major proportions. But we are left in the dark about which of the local floods later became known as *the* flood.

The fact that in the ancient flood stories the water covered all the known parts of the world should not lead one to the conclusion that the flood was a *universal* flood. Stories of floods come from many parts of the world. It is unwarranted, however, to lump all these stories together and claim that they refer to the *same, universal* flood. There is no evidence that allows one to draw this conclusion.

In the ancient world view there was no limit to the amount of rain that could fall, since there was an unlimited supply of water stored in the heavens above and an equally unlimited supply of water stored in the fountains beneath the earth. Hence, when time went on, the magnitude of the flood could expand beyond all limits and higher and higher mountains could be covered. The ancient world view offered no restraint here.

It is therefore reasonable that the story expanded when time went on and that the ark should land in higher and higher places. The J-account does not mention a mountain at all. The Gilgamesh epic lets the ark come to rest on the Nisir mountains in Kurdistan. In the prose account of 275 B.C. the ark comes to rest in Armenia; the text states that parts of it can be found in the mountains of the Gordyeans in Armenia. The P-account mentions the Ararat mountains in Armenia.

It would be wrong to chide the P-version for alleged exaggerations: since these "exaggerations" are in line with what other flood stories offer. If it wanted to speak about the *same* events as the non-Biblical accounts, it had to present the *same* facts. The importance of the message is not in the facts themselves, but in the *interpretation* of these facts, as we shall see in a moment.

Neither should the P-version be chided for the long duration of the flood. Different flood stories give different lengths for the duration of the flood. The long duration in the P-version hangs together with P's cosmology and with the apocalyptic character of P's flood account.

5. Comparison of the P- and J-accounts of the flood.

Now that the two flood stories have been discussed separately and have been compared with non-Biblical flood accounts, it should be borne in mind that in our Bible they are purposely joined together in an editorial process. Apparently the editor was of the opinion that the two stories had a common theological basis and a common theological message. We saw that this was indeed the case, they have in common the message of sin and grace.

But there is more. The two stories have all but some details in common. That they are joined together means that the discrepancies and inconsistencies should be ignored and that the common message should be stressed. As long as that is understood, there is no difficulty.

Difficulties arise, however, when one tries to talk oneself out of these discrepancies. Especially those who are firm believers in the doctrine of verbal inspiration are apt to succumb to such efforts. To those who do, it can only be said that they try to be wiser than the Biblical writers and editors. For it is unthinkable that the editor who put the two flood stories together would not have seen the discrepancies between them. Apparently, however, they did not bother him at all. As good Biblical scholars we should follow in his footsteps.

But, might someone ask, does not this attitude let the doctrine of verbal inspiration fall by the wayside? Not in the least. What should be done is to formulate the doctrine of verbal inspiration in such a manner that inconsistencies and discrepancies in the Biblical account can be *tolerated*. This may require abandoning some cherished theological positions but is basically not difficult. It would be very unwise to tie the certainty of our theological knowledge to our skill in removing discrepancies in the Biblical account!

Why was the story of the flood taken over by the Biblical writers? It may have been that the story goes back to a very ancient Hebrew tradition. But it may also be that it was taken over later, perhaps for the following reasons:

1. The story was so widespread and so generally accepted, that it was important to emphasize that the event was *not outside*

of God's activity but formed an integral part of it. As such the story rightly belongs together with the story of creation, which tells that the beginning of the world around us was also an integral part of God's acts.

2. The story provided the demarcation line between the early created world and the world that Israel knew. It was therefore worth-while to dwell upon it in some detail.

3. The story provides an opportunity to illustrate the message of sin and grace, of God's wrath over sin and God's grace toward sinners.

In order to make the flood story part of the Biblical account, its content had to be altered considerably. Its crudely polytheistic character was eliminated and instead God became the only actor of the drama.

The J-account of the flood is much less spectacular than the P-account. It has no high mountains upon which the ark comes to rest and the flood does not last as long as in the P-account. Biblical scholars know that J has little inclination toward the spectacular. According to him God does not work publicly, but in a hidden manner, either in and through events or in and through the hearts and minds of man. For that reason one would not expect a spectacular account from him.

P apparently does not share this restraint, perhaps for the following reasons:

1. He seems to go back to traditions outside Israel.

2. He purposely pictures the flood as a catastrophe of apocalyptic proportions. This blends perfectly with his world view and with his account of creation.

3. It helps to accentuate the seriousness of human sin as well as the miracle of God's grace.

Does all this mean that the Biblical account is to be considered historically untrue? Not at all, for we have seen that there is a sound basis for a *local* flood. But neither J nor P are interested in reporting about a large flood *as such*. They are interested in incorporating the story of the flood into the Biblical message of sin and grace. Both J and P see the flood as God's judgment over sin, but for the reasons mentioned above, the account given by P takes almost apocalyptical proportions. Both J and P see the salvation of Noah and his family as an act of God's grace.

We may also put it as follows: In a story like the flood one can distinguish between the "facts" and the "interpretation." The Biblical account of the flood has the "facts" in common with other flood accounts, and these "facts" as such are not "God's word." What makes the Biblical flood account "God's word" is the "interpretation" of the "facts." This interpretation gives the message of sin and grace and this message is as binding as ever. If we draw our attention away from the unusual and the spectacular and direct it toward the *message of judgment and grace* that Gen. 6-8 offers, we have not suffered a loss. We scored a gain, for we have then understood what message the flood story brings.

REFERENCES:

[1] Gerhard von Rad, see Chapter 3.

[2] Alan Richardson, see Chapter 3.

[3] Hellmuth Frey, see Chapter 3.

[4] D. Winton Thomas, Editor, *Documents From Old Testament Times*, Thomas Nelson and Sons Ltd., London, 1962.

[5] André Parrot, *Déluge et Arche de Noé*, Delachaux and Niestlé S. A., Neuchatel/Paris.

[6] D. Bonhoeffer, *Nachfolge*, Chr. Kaiser Verlag, München, 1937. Appeared in English translation under the title: "The Cost of Discipleship," S.C.M. Press, London.

Covenant with Noah
Noah's Blessing and Curse

1. The Text. Gen. 9 (P and J).

1a. Covenant with Noah (P), Gen. 9:1-17

(1) And God blessed Noah and his sons, and said unto them, Be fruitful, and multiply, and replenish the earth. (2) And the fear of you and the dread of you shall be upon every beast of the earth, and upon every fowl of the air, upon all that moveth upon the earth, and upon all the fishes of the sea; into your hand are they delivered. (3) Every moving thing that liveth shall be meat for you; even as the green herb have I given you all things. (4) But flesh with the life thereof, which is the blood thereof, shall ye not eat. (5) And surely your blood of your lives will I require; at the hand of every beast will I require it, and at the hand of man; at the hand of every man's brother will I require the life of man. (6) Whoso sheddeth man's blood, by man shall his blood be shed: for in the image of God made he man. (7) And you, be ye fruitful, and multiply; bring forth abundantly in the earth, and multiply therein.

(8) And God spake unto Noah, and to his sons with him, saying, (9) And I, behold, I establish my covenant with you, and with your seed after you; (10) And with every living crea-

ture that is with you, of the fowl, of the cattle, and of every beast of the earth with you; from all that go out of the ark, to every beast of the earth. (11) And I will establish my covenant with you; neither shall all flesh be cut off any more by the waters of a flood; neither shall there any more be a flood to destroy the earth. (12) And God said, This is the token of the covenant which I make between me and you and every living creature that is with you, for perpetual generations: (13) I do set my bow in the cloud, and it shall be for a token of a covenant between me and the earth. (14) And it shall come to pass, when I bring a cloud over the earth, that the bow shall be seen in the cloud: (15) And I will remember my covenant, which is between me and you and every living creature of all flesh; and the waters shall no more become a flood to destroy all flesh. (16) And the bow shall be in the cloud; and I will look upon it, that I may remember the everlasting covenant between God and every living creature of all flesh that is upon the earth. (17) And God said unto Noah, This is the token of the covenant, which I have established between me and all flesh that is upon the earth.

1b. Noah's blessing and curse (J), Gen. 9:18-27

(18) And the sons of Noah, that went forth of the ark, were Shem, and Ham, and Japheth: and Ham is the father of Canaan. (19) These are the three sons of Noah: and of them was the whole earth overspread.

(20) And Noah began to be an husbandman, and he planted a vineyard: (21) And he drank of the wine, and was drunken; and he was uncovered within his tent. (22) And Ham, the father of Canaan, saw the nakedness of his father, and told his two brethren without. (23) And Shem and Japheth took a

garment, and laid it upon both their shoulders, and went back-
ward, and covered the nakedness of their father; and their faces
were backward, and they saw not their father's nakedness. (24)
And Noah awoke from his wine, and knew what his younger
son had done unto him. (25) And he said, Cursed be Canaan;
a servant of servants shall he be unto his brethren. (26) And
he said, Blessed be the Lord God of Shem; and Canaan shall
be his servant. (27) God shall enlarge Japheth, and he shall
dwell in the tents of Shem; and Canaan shall be his servant.

1c. Part of the "book of generations" (P) Gen. 9:28-29

(28) And Noah lived after the flood three hundred and
fifty years. (29) And all the days of Noah were nine hundred
and fifty years: and he died.

2. Discussion.

2a. God's covenant with Noah (P)

The world after the flood is the world that Israel knows.
It is a world quite different from the world described in Gen. 1.
The perfect creation has been disturbed: violence and murder
reign and the peace among God's creatures is gone. And that
poses several questions which P tries to answer[1]. They are the
following:

1. Does the command: "be fruitful" still hold under the
new circumstances? That does not speak for itself. True enough,
to multiply and to occupy the earth is one of man's most elementary urges. But it is not certain that this urge is still according to God's will; it might be another example of man's willfullness. For that reason it is important to the author that the
first word in the new era after the flood is a word of *blessing,*
coupled to a repetition of the command.

2. Does the command that gives man to rule over the animals still hold? Again, that does not speak for itself. It might well be that man in his sinful state would not be considered fit to rule the animals. It is therefore important to the author that this command is specifically renewed. But it is conceded that this rule is now more a rule by fear than a benevolent rule: the fear of man and the dread for man will be upon all animals[3].

3. Does God's command that gave to man every seed-bearing herb and the fruit of every tree for food, still hold? It does, for the command is renewed. It is even extended; man is now also free to eat animals. This indicates that the paradise-like atmosphere of Gen. 1 is gone. It will not reappear until the end of time (Isaiah 11). One restriction is made, however: the blood of animals should not be eaten. According to ancient tradition, life was thought to be specifically located in the blood. As an acknowledgment that all life belongs to God, man should abstain from eating "life," that is, "blood."

4. Is man's life still sacred? Despite violence and bloodshed it still is, and for that reason it is important to have this mentioned specifically. God holds anybody, man or beast, responsible for killing a man. And he who kills, be it man or beast, must answer for it with his own life. For, even under the changed circumstances, *God is* still the *owner* of all life.

5. Who is going to avenge the spilling of blood? The answer is: "Man." The text formulates this in a very condensed, archaic manner: "Whoso sheddeth man's blood, by man shall his blood be shed: for in the image of God made he man." Possibly this expression originally restricted the blood revenge to the immediate killer and forbade killing the killer's relatives as a revenge for the murder committed. But in its present for-

mulation it gives this task not to an individual but to the human community at large.

To emphasize that man's life is still sacred for God, it is here repeated what was said in Gen. 1: "in the image of God made he man." This indicates once again that P does not consider the image of God to have been lost by sin.

The statements indicate that the era after the flood is an era of God's forbearance, blessing and grace, despite human sin. God has not withdrawn Himself from the world because of human sin but keeps coming with His *demands* and with His *promises*. On this point J and P are in full agreement. They also agree that God has not relinquished His rule over the world but keeps exercising it.

God makes a new covenant with *all mankind* and with *all living creatures* by giving the solemn promise: "No more shall the earth be destroyed by a flood." As a token of this God sets the rainbow.

A covenant serves to clarify an obscure judicial situation between two groups or two individuals. Usually the two partners are unequal. Here the two partners are God and mankind, as unequal as they can possibly be. But, nevertheless, the covenant exists: God will be with the coming era, and will guarantee the existence of mankind and of all life.

The word "bow" corresponds to a word in the original that is otherwise translated as "war bow." As such, the token of the rainbow indicates to man that God has set His war bow aside and intends to keep peace with man. This gracious relationship toward man shows itself in the stability of the natural order and in God's guarantee of man's existence[1].

The text does not say that there were no rainbows before.

A rainbow is a natural phenomenon that will be with us as long as the sun shines and rain falls. What is new here is that from now on the rainbow is seen as the carrier of a promise: that the earth shall no more be destroyed by water, but that God guarantees the natural order.

This chapter of priestly theology can only be understood if its aetiological aspects are recognized[1]. Why does the stability of the natural order continue, despite human violence? Why is human existence still blessed, despite human sin? The answer is that this is God's grace toward man and God's forbearance with man. *Without* God's promise and blessing, this world would be lost. God's promise and blessing *keep* this world, despite human sin and violence. For it is the world in which God will show His salvation for all mankind.

2b. Noah's blessing and curse (J)

This story, which belongs to J, aetiologically answers an important question of Israel's existence: the presence of other people in the promised land. We follow here mainly the interpretation given by von Rad[1].

The section is difficult to interpret. At first sight everything looks simple. The story starts with the end of the flood and tells that Shem, Ham and Japheth, from whom all mankind descend, came out of the ark with Noah. But already in the beginning the name of Canaan, the son of Ham is mentioned. At the end of the story the problem centers around Canaan, Shem and Japheth. And, what is more, they are no longer the forefathers of all mankind but seem to refer to different peoples in Palestine. More about that later.

Noah plants a vineyard. When the vines have grown up and have borne fruit, he makes wine. Of course, he is not accustomed to the power of this new product, becomes drunk and lies naked in his tent. He thus commits the acts that were common to the Canaanitic fertility cult: drunkenness and exhibitionism (Richardson[2]).

Noah's nakedness is seen by Ham, the father of Canaan, who tells his brothers. These go inside the tent and cover their father. They carefully walk into the tent in such a manner that they do not see their father's nakedness. When Noah wakes up and learns about what happened, he curses Canaan, blesses the God of Shem and also utters a blessing for Japheth.

At first sight that does not make much sense. If it is really true that Ham saw his father's nakedness and made fun of it, then *he* should be cursed and not his son Canaan, who could not be held responsible for his father's deed.

Alan Richardson[2] suggests that the curse does not so much refer to a *person* as to a *culture*. It is the Canaanitic culture, culminating in fertility cults and temple prostitution that is cursed. This seems to be a worth-while suggestion, though it does not fully clarify the situation.

To clarify the situation further, some interpreters have suggested that originally the story dealt with *Canaan* and not with Ham[1]. According to them it was *Canaan* who discovered Noah lying naked in the tent and it was *he* who made fun of it. All one has to do in this case is to eliminate in verse 22: "Ham, the father of" and the story reads: "And Canaan saw the nakedness of his father." According to them the name Ham is introduced to make the connection with the flood story.

The actual actors in the story are then Canaan, Shem and Japheth. But now Shem and Japheth do not refer to two of the three forefathers of mankind but to two *peoples* in *Palestine,* who live there together with the Canaanites. Shem is, of course, Israel, but who is Japheth? It must be a people that lives in the same geographical area as Israel, for it is said that "Japheth shall dwell in the tents of Shem." Together with Israel, it rules over the Canaanites and keeps them in servitude. This narrows down the possibilities sufficiently to make a sensible choice. According to the above interpreters "Japheth" refers to the Philistines[1].

The story thus gives an answer to an uncomfortable question for Israel: "Why was Israel not alone in the promised land?" There were the Canaanites and the Philistines. The latter had settled into the coastal area of Palestine at about the same time that the Israelites entered Palestine from the east, whereas the Canaanites came there much earlier. Both the Philistines and the Israelites ruled over the Canaanites and all occupied the same territory. How was this possible, when Israel laid claim to *all* of Palestine (compare e.g. the book of Joshua)?

It is this question that the story answers for them. That the Philistines and the Canaanites occupy the same territory as Israel is part of God's great plan, established long ago. Even Noah prophesied already that Japheth would live in the tents of Shem. Noah already indicated that Canaan would be "the servant of servants" (the meanest servant) of both.

Canaan's subservient role follows from his unchaste behavior, here exemplified by Canaan's attitude toward the naked Noah. The story says "and (Noah) knew what his younger son had done unto him" and thereby hints that what happened was more than mere looking. The Old Testament often mentions with horror the sexual perversion of the Canaanites, especially their temple prostitution and their fertility rites.

It is interesting to note that Shem is not praised for his good attitude. Instead, "the God of Shem" is praised.

The sentence about Japheth is not a Messianic prophecy, as some think. Neither does it mean, as some church fathers have suggested, that Japheth shall once have part in Shem's religion. It simply means that Shem (Israel) and Japheth (Philistines) shall occupy the same territory.

Noah, though righteous, is not exalted by the author. He is pictured as he is, a sinner, but a sinner reconciled with God and walking with God. Noah is not condemned for being drunk. He had to experience first before he could know that wine must be approached carefully.

Some interpreters think that the planting of the vineyard and the invention of winemaking partly lifted the curse of the ground. As said before, that seems somewhat farfetched. Nevertheless, it must not be forgotten that vineyards were treasured highly in Israel. To have a vineyard, to use its fruit and to rest in the peace that its shade gives, was for the Israelites the summit of happiness and a foreshadowing of the Messianic era.

To sum it up: Gen. 9:18-27 does not primarily deal with the message of sin and grace but answers disquieting questions about Israel's existence. It should not be used to justify the exploitation and subjection of other races by the white race.

2c. Part of the "book of generations" (P)

The era of Noah is hereby closed. To emphasize this, the editor ends with a statement about Noah's life after the flood and his death. This is a quotation from P's book of generations, encountered before in Gen. 5, and to be encountered once again in Gen. 10 and 11.

REFERENCES:
[1]Gerhard von Rad, see Chapter 3.
[2]Alan Richardson, see Chapter 3.
[3]Hellmuth Frey, see Chapter 3.

CHAPTER TEN

The List of Nations
The Genealogy of Abram

1. The Text. Gen. 10; 11:10-27, 31, 32.

1a. The list of nations according to P. Gen. 10:1a, 2-5, 6-7, 20, 22-23, 31-32.

(1a) Now these are the generations of the sons of Noah.

(2) The sons of Japheth; Gomer, and Magog, and Madai, and Javan, and Tubal, and Meschech, and Tiras. (3) And the sons of Gomer; Ashkenaz, and Riphath, and Togarmah. (4) And the sons of Javan; Elishah, and Tarshish, Kittim, and Dodanim. (5) By these were the isles of the Gentiles divided in their lands; every one after his tongue, after their families, in their nations.

(6) And the sons of Ham; Cush, and Mizraim, and Phut, and Canaan. (7) And the sons of Cush; Seba, and Havilah, and Sabtah, and Raamah, and Sabtechah: and the sons of Raamah; Sheba, and Dedan. (20) These are the sons of Ham, after their families, after their tongues, in their countries, and in their nations.

(22) The children of Shem; Elam, and Asshur, and Arphaxad, and Lud, and Aram. (23) And the children of Aram; Uz, and Hul, and Gether, and Mash. (31) These are the sons

of Shem, after their families, after their tongues, in their lands, after their nations.

(32) These are the families of the sons of Noah, after their generations, in their nations: and by these were the nations divided in the earth after the flood.

1b. The list of nations according to J. Gen. 10:1b, 8-14, 15-19, 21, 24-30.

(1b) . . . Shem, Ham, and Japheth: and unto them were sons born after the flood.

(8) And Cush begat Nimrod: he began to be a mighty one in the earth. (9) He was a mighty hunter before the Lord: wherefore it is said, Even as Nimrod the mighty hunter before the Lord. (10) And the beginning of his kingdom was Babel, and Erech, and Accad, and Calneh, in the land of Shinar. (11) Out of that land went forth Asshur, and builded Nineveh, and the city Rehoboth, and Calah, and Resen between Nineveh and Calah: (12) the same is a great city. (13) And Mizraim begat Ludim, and Anamim, and Lehabim, and Naphtuhim, (14) and Pathrusim, and Casluhim, and Caphtorim (out of whom came Philistim).

(15) And Canaan begat Sidon his first-born, and Heth, (16) and the Jebusite, and the Amorite, and the Girgasite, (17) and the Hivite, and the Arkite, and the Sinite, (18) and the Arvadite, and the Zemarite, and the Hamathite: and afterward were the families of the Canaanites spread abroad. (19) And the border of the Canaanites was from Sidon, as thou comest to Gerar, unto Gaza; as thou goest, unto Sodom, and Gomorrah, and Admah, and Zeboim, even unto Lasha.

(21) Unto Shem also, the father of all the children of Eber, the brother of Japheth the elder, even to him were children

*born. (24) And Arphaxad begat Salah; and Salah begat Eber.
(25) And unto Eber were born two sons: the name of the one
was Peleg; for in his days was the earth divided; and his brother's name was Joktan. (26) And Joktan begat Almodad, and
Sheleph, and Hazarmaveth, and Jerah, (27) and Hadoram,
and Uzal and Diklah, (28) and Obal, and Abimael, and Sheba,
(29) and Ophir, and Havilah, and Jobab: all these were the
sons of Joktan. (30) And their dwelling was from Mesha, as
thou goest unto Sephar a mount of the East.*

(Gen. 10:14. The statement "out of whom came Philistim" is located behind "Casluhim" in the King James version.)

1c. The genealogy of Abram according to P. Gen. 11:10-27, 31-32.

*(10) These are the generations of Shem: Shem was an hun-
dred years old, and begat Arphaxad two years after the flood:
(11) And Shem lived after he begat Arphaxad five hundred
years, and begat sons and daughters. (12) And Arphaxad lived
five and thirty years, and begat Salah: (13) And Arphaxad
lived after he begat Salah four hundred and three years, and
begat sons and daughters. (14) And Salah lived thirty years,
and begat Eber: (15) And Salah lived after he begat Eber four
hundred and three years, and begat sons and daughters. (16)
And Eber lived four and thirty years, and begat Peleg: (17)
And Eber lived after he begat Peleg four hundred and thirty
years, and begat sons and daughters. (18) And Peleg lived
thirty years, and begat Reu: (19) And Peleg lived after he
begat Reu two hundred and nine years, and begat sons and
daughters. (20) And Reu lived two and thirty years, and begat
Serug: (21) And Reu lived after he begat Serug two hundred
and seven years, and begat sons and daughters. (22) And Serug*

lived thirty years, and begat Nahor: (23) And Serug lived after he begat Nahor two hundred years, and begat sons and daughters. (24) And Nahor lived nine and twenty years, and begat Terah: (25) And Nahor lived after he begat Terah an hundred and nineteen years, and begat sons and daughters. (26) And Terah lived seventy years, and begat Abram, Nahor, and Haran.

(27) Now these are the generations of Terah: Terah begat Abram, Nahor, and Haran; and Haran begat Lot. (31) And Terah took Abram his son, and Lot the son of Haran his son's son, and Sarai his daughter in law, his son Abram's wife; and they went forth with them from Ur of the Chaldees, to go into the land of Canaan; and they came unto Haran, and dwelt there. (32) And the days of Terah were two hundred and five years: and Terah died in Haran.

(Gen. 11:28-30 belongs to J, see next chapter.)

2. Discussion of the list of nations.

The list of nations in Chapter 10 consists of a P-part and a J-part. The P-part is more or less complete but the J-part is fragmentary. For a good understanding the texts should be separated first. We have followed von Rad[1] in this.

In discussing this list, care should be taken that no concepts are introduced that are alien to the text. For example, the nations are not ordered according to their racial origin, nor are they ordered according to linguistic criteria. They are pictured according to their historical and political interrelationships[1-3].

Furthermore, the nations are represented as *persons*. That they should be considered as nations nevertheless follows from the facts that the ages are missing and that the statement "and he died" is not found in this chapter.

2a. The list of nations according to P.

Let us illustrate what was said about nations represented as persons[1]. Canaan represents the Canaanites, Cush is Ethiopia, Mizraim is Egypt and Phut is Lybia.

Why are these four listed as sons of Ham, even though the Canaanites were of Semitic stock? Because politically they belonged to Egypt at the time that is pictured here. That is, political relationship determines the position of a nation in this list and not racial origin.

As an example of the fact that the list is pictured at a certain time, consider the Hittite empire that reached its peak of power around 1390 B.C. The list does not say any word about this empire but mentions instead a number of nations that are listed under Japheth. They are nations that replaced the Hittite empire around 1200 B.C. during the Aegean invasion.

Gomer, Magog and Tubal are peoples from the Black Sea region. Javan represents the Greeks. The "sons of Javan" are Greek colonists, Elishah is thought to be somewhere in Cyprus, Kittim also in Cyprus, Dodanim (a better reading is Rodanim) represents the Rhodians, Tarshish is a Greek colony in Spain. The Greek colonists are "people of the isles or coast" mentioned in verse 5 (A. Richardson[2]).

In addition, the list mentions some people that come into prominence around 800-700 B.C. One of them is Madai, representing the Medes. The list thus gives sometimes pictures that are superimposed upon each other.

If one is not aware of such possibilities as were just mentioned, one is bound to find discrepancies and inconsistencies everywhere. If one learns the rules that were used by the composers of the list, those discrepancies disappear.

One could go on in the same manner. The "sons of Cush" seem to correspond to tribes in Arabia. Elam represents the Elamites, Asshur represents the Assyrians, Aram represents the Syrians. The latter three are all presented as sons of Shem.

The theological importance of the list is in the first place that it pictures the multitude of nations as the fulfillment of the command: "Be fruitful and multiply." This blessing has been fulfilled and the list reflects amazement over the resulting abundance. The multitude of nations and the complexities of the political and historical relationship are seen as God's creation. As such, Gen. 10 rightly belongs together with Gen. 1.

By relating all these peoples back to Noah's sons, and hence to Noah, the list sees these nations as sharing the covenant that God made with Noah. It sees God's gracious will as extending toward these peoples. Finally, the list stresses the essential unity of all mankind.

Israel is missing from the table of nations. It did not consider itself as the center of the universe like Babylon. Israel did not have a high opinion of itself. Israel is not important historically or dominant politically, and it is not elected by God for that reason. For Israel it is important what God *does to* them and *with* them and not what they *are*.

Here we see once more how faith in the God of Israel means a radical break with mythology in all its forms. It prevents Israel from having a very high opinion of itself, in direct contrast with the mythologies with which other peoples surrounded themselves.

Since Israel is missing, one cannot conclude from the covenant with Noah that God's special relationship with Israel also extends to the other nations. That they share in the benefits of this relationship follows from God's promise to Abram: "In thee shall all families of the earth be blessed." That is not written in Gen. 10, however, and should not be read into the text.

2b. The list of nations according to J.

This list is fragmentary. Apparently the editor who joined J and P together, eliminated major parts of J's list. For example, the list of Japheth's descendants is missing; it is hard to believe that it was not part of J's list originally.

Ham's descendants are again listed as Cush (Ethiopia), Mizraim (Egypt) and Canaan. From Mizraim come the Philistines and from Canaan come the Hittites (Heth). Since the Philistines and the Hittites were indogermanic peoples, it is clear that J does not use racial origin as a criterion for ordering his list. Since the Hittites lived in Palestine during Abram's time, it seems reasonable to assume that geographical and political criteria determine the position of peoples in J's list like in P.

P's list covers a much larger geographical area than J's list[1]. The latter stays close to Palestine, whereas P's view ranges from Spain, the Greek islands and the Black Sea area to southern Arabia and deep into Africa!

The name Nimrod poses as particular difficulty. He is mentioned as the great despotic ruler and the proverbial hunter. The expression "before the Lord" means something like "on earth" and does not necessarily indicate that Nimrod stood in a special relationship to God and had a special knowledge of God[2].

But who is Nimrod? If Cush is Ethiopia and Mizraim is Egypt, how then can Cush's son Nimrod have become the mighty ruler of the Euphrates-Tigris valley? Some interpreters have suggested that Nimrod represents the Egyptian King

Amenophis III (1411-1375 B.C.), who claims to have extended his empire down to the Euphrates river and who boasts of great lion and wild bull hunts in that area. In that case Nimrod could at least be considered a descendant of Ham. Others have suggested that Nimrod refers to the Babylonian God Ninurta, the god of hunting. But what has this then to do with Ham? These things are difficult to unravel.

Some translators read that Nimrod founded Nineveh, but that is unfounded. The King James text seems to be correct: Asshur moves out of Shinar (Babylonia) to found Nineveh.

The Caphtorim are the inhabitants of Crete (Caphtor) which is here thought of as an Egyptian dependency. The Philistines are usually said to have come from Crete, and for that reason it is generally assumed that the words in brackets in verse 14 should follow Caphtorim, not Casluhim (A. Richardson[2]). This text improvement has been adopted in section 1b.

The sons of Shem include Arabian tribes. Eber refers to the Hebrews, which seems to have been the name by which other peoples called the Israelites.

The theological importance of J's list of nations is similar to P's list. It sees the multitude of nations as sharing Noah's promises and as a fulfillment of the command: "Be fruitful and multiply." It stresses the essential unity of all mankind.

3. The genealogy of Abram (P).

The names found in this list are thought of as *persons*. The list gives the age at which each person dies and the age at which the oldest son is born. The ages gradually grow smaller as time goes on and become more "normal." Apparently this is done to demonstrate a marked decrease in the vitality of mankind.

The Septuagint and the Samaritan text show differences in chronology, however.

The list also seems to reflect the early history of the Middle East (von Rad[1]). At the end of the second millenium B.C. the Arameans entered western Mesopotamia and the northern part of Syria. Later the same wave of immigrants (the Chaldeans) moved into Ur. During the same wave of immigration the Israelites seem to have entered Palestine. As a reflection of this, the list mentions the names Haran, Serug, Nahor, Terah and Peleg, which are references to towns in the area around Haran (better written as Charan). Also Ur is mentioned as the place from which Terah departed to Charan.

The genealogy says that Terah and his relatives were on their way to Canaan but gives no reason why they took the circuitous route via Charan. Would it not have been much easier to take the direct route? A look on the map shows, however, that this would have brought them through the great Arabian Desert. For that reason the circuitous route could well have been the easiest and the safest one. It is known that Charan was a center where many caravan roads met; the name probably means "crossroads."

The list does not say anything about Terah's son Nahor. Later sections of Genesis, that belong to J, show, however, that Nahor's descendants also lived in Charan. Hence, either Terah's whole clan moved with him to Charan or the J-version only knows Charan as the place where Israel's ancestors came from. Many interpreters consider the latter to be most likely.

The name Abram is a contraction of Abiram, which means: "the (divine) father is exalted." The later name "Abraham" is explained in the text as "the father of a multitude of nations."

As said before, the decreasing ages demonstrate the decrease in man's vitality. At the same time the background for Isaac's remarkable birth is prepared.

The genealogy of Abram is preceded by the list of nations. Why was it not sufficient to state that Abram, and hence Israel, descended directly from Adam? Why are the nations first traced back to Noah and from there to Adam and then, but only then, Abram's ancestors are traced through the list of nations? There must be a good reason for this.

The reason seems to be the mystery of Abram's election[1]. Abram, and Israel with him, was elected *out of all nations,* so that in him all the nations on earth might be blessed. Was this because of Abram's merit? No, it was God's free decision to make a new start with Abram. Because of the mystery of this decision, the list of nations is so important to the author. It emphasizes the *freedom* of God's election. But it should be understood once again that freedom does not mean arbitrariness.

REFERENCES:

[1]Gerhard von Rad, see Chapter 3.
[2]Alan Richardson, see Chapter 3.
[3]Hellmuth Frey, see Chapter 3.

CHAPTER ELEVEN

The Tower of Babel
The Election of Abram

1. The Text. Gen. 11:1-9; 28-30; 12:1-9 (J).
1a. The tower of Babel (J). Gen. 11:1-9.

(1) And the whole earth was of one language, and of one speech. (2) And it came to pass, as they journeyed from the east, that they found a plain in the land of Shinar; and they dwelt there. (3) And they said one to another, Go to, let us make brick, and burn them throughly. And they had brick for stone, and slime had they for morter. (4) And they said, Go to, let us build us a city and a tower, whose top may reach unto heaven; and let us make us a name, lest we be scattered abroad upon the face of the whole earth. (5) And the Lord came down to see the city and the tower, which the children of men builded. (6) And the Lord said, Behold, the people is one, and they have all one language; and this they begin to do: and now nothing will be restrained from them, which they have imagined to do. (7) Go to, let us go down, and there confound their language, that they may not understand one another's speech. (8) So the Lord scattered them abroad from thence upon the face of all the earth: and they left off to build the city. (9) Therefore is the name of it called Babel; because

the Lord did there confound the language of all the earth: and from thence did the Lord scatter them abroad upon the face of all the earth.

1b. The calling of Abram (J). Gen. 11:28-30, 12:1-4a.

Gen. 11:28-30. (28) And Haran died before his father Terah in the land of his nativity, in Ur of the Chaldees. (29) And Abram and Nahor took them wives: the name of Abram's wife was Sarai; and the name of Nahor's wife, Milcah, the daughter of Haran, the father of Milcah, and the father of Iscah. (30) But Sarai was barren; she had no child.

Gen. 12:1-4a. (1) Now the Lord had said unto Abram, Get thee out of thy country, and from thy kindred, and from thy father's house, unto a land that I will shew thee: (2) And I will make of thee a great nation, and I will bless thee, and make thy name great; and thou shalt be a blessing: (3) And I will bless them that bless thee, and curse him that curseth thee: and in thee shall all families of the earth be blessed. (4a) So Abram departed, as the Lord had spoken unto him.

1c. An addition from P. Gen. 12:4b.

. . . (4b) and Lot went with him: and Abram was seventy and five years old when he departed out of Haran.

1d. Abram's entry into Canaan (J). Gen. 12:5-9.

(5) And Abram took Sarai his wife, and Lot his brother's son, and all their substance that they had gathered, and the souls that they had gotten in Haran; and they went forth to go into the land of Canaan; and into the land of Canaan they came.

*(6) And Abram passed through the land unto the place of
Sichem, unto the plain of Moreh. And the Canaanite was then
in the land. (7) And the Lord appeared unto Abram, and said,
Unto thy seed will I give this land: and there builded he an
altar unto the Lord, who appeared unto him. (8) And he removed from thence unto a mountain on the east of Bethel, and
pitched his tent, having Bethel on the west, and Hai on the east:
and there he builded an altar unto the Lord, and called upon
the name of the Lord. (9) And Abram journeyed, going on
still toward the south.*

2. Discussion of the tower of Babel account (J).

This section of Genesis belongs to J. If one ascribes to the
four-tradition theory, the text must be ascribed to L.

The list of nations sees the many peoples with their many
tongues as a sign of God's creative power and will. But another
point of view is presented here: the same phenomenon is now
seen as God's judgment over man's willfullness. The phenomena of human life and history are thus seen in a double light,
once as a sign of God's creative will and once as a judgment.
This is similar to what was encountered in Gen. 2 and 3.

The story starts with an invention. Man, still of one language, emigrates to the Euphrates-Tigris valley and settles there.
They then invent baking bricks, and, by using asphalt for
mortar, they build great buildings and a great town. That is,
culture, as we know it, develops.

Man is rightly proud of his newly found power and the
great work is started with enthusiasm. They want to make a
name for themselves and they want to band together for fear
of being scattered over the earth. The tower that they are going

to build is meant to "reach into heaven." That should not be seen as an attempt to reach "heaven" by human means, but more as an indication how high the tower is going to be.

The author sees this as a sign of human willfullness. In the Bible it is always God who makes a great name for men like Abram, Moses, David, etc. Man's striving to make a great name *for himself* is thus seen as a *sin,* as a rebellion against God's love and care.

And then the story takes an ironic twist. They have been working so hard to build something big and high and, nevertheless, it is so small and puny in God's eyes, that God has to come down to see it better![3]

God, however, takes man's striving seriously. What they are now doing is only the beginning; if they continue, there will be no end to it. They will go wherever their imagination may lead them; there will be no restraint to man's striving. God decides to prevent this by confounding their language, so that they can no longer understand each other. This is more a preventive measure than an actual punishment. It is taken to avoid more drastic action later. As a consequence, they stop building the city and scatter abroad.

The story is full of irony. The men say: "Go to, let us make brick" and "Go to, let us build a city and a tower" and therefore God says: "Go to, let us go down, and there confound their language." As before, the "us" is not a "pluralis majestatis" but may be interpreted as "God and His heavenly court."

It would be wrong to assume that this story aetiologically *explains* why there are so many peoples and languages. Instead, the story sees the many peoples and languages as a consequence and as a sign of man's willful striving, of man's rebellion against God.

The story ends with a word play. The name Bab-El means "gate of God." The inhabitants of Babylon see their town as a gate through which their mighty God enters to meet the men to whom he addresses his message. It is a name filled with nobility and pride. But the author hears in it the Hebrew word "balal" which means "confusion." As an answer to man's pride the Bible thus states: "this is not the gate of God, this is confusion."

The story of the tower of Babel poses the following serious question[1]: Is the relation between God and the nations broken completely and has God definitely rejected them in his wrath? If the story of the tower of Babel were the end of the "Urgeschichte," the first part of Genesis would end in darkness and despair.

But it is not the end. It sets the beginning of a new starting point: the election of Abram. God has not rejected the nations, for in Abram "all families of the earth shall be blessed." The calling of Abram rightly belongs to the "Urgeschichte," since it answers the question posed by the story of the tower of Babel.

God has a history with man. It is not a history of which man can be proud, for it is a history of sin and rebellion, followed by God's punishment. But God does not leave man alone in his guilt and his punishment. Despite human sin He keeps mankind and starts anew. For that reason the tower of Babel episode is not the end but the starting point of a new era: God's covenant with Abram.

3. The election of Abram (J).

With one small exception (Gen. 12:4b) the beginning of Gen. 12 belongs to J. It tells how Abram was chosen by God.

3a. The calling of Abram.

First the background is given: the account starts with Terah and his three sons: Haran, Nahor and Abram. Haran dies relatively young. Many interpreters consider the addition: "in Ur of the Chaldees" as a later harmonization effort. According to them, J only knows Charan as the land of nativity of Abram and his ancestors[1].

Nahor marries his brother Haran's daughter, Abram marries Sarai. The father of Sarai is not mentioned. Probably J also considered her to be Abram's sister (Gen. 20:12), but did not want to express this[1]. The author adds that Sarai was childless, thus preparing for the enormity of God's promise and for the miracle of Isaac's birth.

God begins his promise to Abram with a command. He must leave his land, his kindred and his father's house, to go to the land that God will show him. He must make a radical break with the past and with everything near to him and must trust himself solely to God's guidance. Only in this manner will Abram be serviceable, only in this manner is God going to make a new beginning that will be important to all mankind.

The command given to Abram is also the command by which Israel knew itself called as a nation. As Abram, they were taken out of the multitude of nations, living in Canaan more or less as foreigners, living not by their own plans but by God's guidance. To them Abram was not only an example, he was also an analogy to Israel's existence before God.

The characteristic word of God's promise to Abram is "blessing." The blessing is first of all a physical one: Abram, married to a barren woman, shall become a great nation. God will make Abram's name great. Abram does not have to do that himself willfully, but God will do it for him. And not only will God bless Abram, but Abram will also be a blessing to others. God's election is not for Abram himself, it is primarily for others. God elects for *service* and His election aims at *all* mankind.

God will be with Abram and protect him. Those who bless him, God will bless, but he who curses him, God will curse. Note that the first is a plural whereas the latter is a singular. The blessings of others will abound and the curses will be few.

"And in thee shall all families of the earth be blessed." The Revised Standard Version reads "and by you all the families of the earth will bless themselves." Both versions are possible but not equally likely. Von Rad[1] chooses for the first version for two reasons. In the first place, he dislikes the idea that such solemn words should be so limited in their meaning. In the second place, God's word spoken to Abram should reach its climax at the end. The first version gives such a climax, but the second version gives an anticlimax. It merely states that God will bless Abram so abundantly that his blessing will become proverbial: "God bless you like He blessed Abram." Adopting the first version then, the promise states that Abram's election is for the benefit of all mankind.

The question is now: "Is Abram serviceable; will he obey God?" He does, he makes the break demanded of him and he departs. Abram believes God's promise despite the circumstances. His wife is barren but Abram believes that God has the power to make him a great nation. That is Abram's righteousness.

3b. A small addition from P.

After Gen. 12:4a the editor has inserted a small section

from P to indicate how radical Abram's break with the past is. According to P, Abram was born when Terah was 70 years old and Terah dies when he is 205 years old. Now we are told that Abram leaves Charan when he is 75 years old, that is 60 years before his father's death! All this is not said arbitrarily but is stated purposely to illustrate how large a step Abram is taking.

3c. Abram's entry into Canaan.

Abram departs with Sarai, his wife, Lot, his brother's son, their slaves (the souls that they had gotten) and with all they have. They go to the land of Canaan and arrive there safely.

In Canaan, Abram is not at home: he is a foreigner, for the Canaanites live there. Abram travels through the country and looks it over. In the plain of Moreh another promise of God comes to Abram: "Unto thy seed I will give this land." Abram believes this promise, and builds an altar for the Lord at that place to commemorate another one of God's great promises.

To Israel this promise is of special importance. It tells them that their living in Canaan is not accidental. It is part of God's great plan, established long ago. Their living in the land is the fulfillment of the promise that God made to Abram.

On and on Abram travels. He pitches his tent between Bethel and Hai and he builds another altar for the Lord and calls upon the name of the Lord. His journey, though seemingly aimless, is not without purpose: he looks over the land that God has promised to his descendants. And he goes in dependence upon the God Who called him and with faith in God's promises.

He continues his journey toward the south of the country, the Negev. Later (Gen. 13:18) he will settle down in the southern countryside, in the plain of Mamre, between Hebron and Beer-sheba.

And so the "Urgeschichte" ends with Abram, the father of all believers. A new beginning is made, a beginning that will be developed in the remainder of the Old Testament. A new hope springs up: God does not leave mankind alone, but aims at man's salvation.

The fulfillment of the promise made to Abram does not lie in Abram himself, but lies beyond Abram in "Him, Whose day Abraham longed to see." But that is written in the New Testament.

REFERENCES:
[1]Gerhard von Rad, see Chapter 3.
[2]Alan Richardson, see Chapter 3.
[3]Hellmuth Frey, see Chapter 3.

CHAPTER TWELVE

The Methods of the Natural Sciences

Having discussed the Genesis text, we now turn to the problem what science can say about the world around us and about its beginning. To do so, we first discuss how the natural sciences operate. We can then look at the structure and the origin of the universe, at the history of the earth and the history of life, at evolution and the origin of life and of man.

1. Observation and measurement[1, 2].

Science is the systematic gathering and processing of sets of "facts." The various sciences differ in what these "facts" are, in how these "facts" are gathered, how they are processed, systematized and presented. The natural sciences take their "facts" from the realm of nature.

These facts are gathered by *observation* and by *measurement*. Observation in general gives qualitative knowledge, whereas measurements generally result in quantitative knowledge. The latter is usually expressed in terms of numbers. Since numbers belong to the realm of mathematics, it is not surprising that mathematics plays a large role in most of the natural sciences.

During the Middle Ages science consisted of quoting the proper "authority"; the Bible, Aristotle, the Church Fathers, etc.

The same method of approach was also used in philosophy and in theology, so that there was an impressive unity of approach in those days. Sometimes the word of the "authority" was based on observation, sometimes it was a mere speculation, sometimes it was patently wrong and sometimes, as in quotations from the Bible, it was misunderstood.

The idea that, in order to understand nature, one cannot quote "authorities," but that one must *observe* and *measure,* came as a great shock to many. Galilei deserves the credit for being the first to articulate this important insight, and he paid for it with many tribulations.

In the Middle Ages Genesis was the proper authority to quote in discussions about the origin of the world and of the universe. At present this is no longer the case. If one wants to know what happened in the past and how these happenings can be interpreted in the light of present knowledge, one must investigate the evidence presently available and search for further evidence. If the Genesis account were an *eyewitness* account, it might still be considered as evidence. As we have seen, however, it is *not* an eyewitness account, but it gives *witness* concerning God the creator. For that reason the Genesis account, though binding theologically, is not binding scientifically. As far as the scientific search for the origin of the earth, of the universe, and of the development of life on earth is concerned, the scientist is completely on his own. He is not limited or restricted by the Genesis account of creation. But if he later wants to *relate* his findings *to his Christian faith,* he is bound by the witness that Genesis gives. To make this clear at the very outset of the discussion avoids confusion later.

We now return to our discussion of the scientific processes of observation and measurement. Some observations can already be made with the unaided senses, but many more can be made by using aids such as telescopes, radiotelescopes, microscopes, mass spectroscopes, etc.

In problems that are investigated in the laboratory, one cannot only observe and measure, but one can also *experiment*. That is, one can vary the initial conditions one by one and then investigate what influence that has on the phenomena under consideration. This is of great help in obtaining a better and more rapid understanding of what is going on.

The final results of such an investigation are usually formulated in terms of "laws." In a qualitative investigation the results are summed up in a short statement, in a quantitative investigation the results are usually summed up in a mathematical equation. Both are known as "laws."

It is obvious that one cannot "experiment" with the structure of the universe or with the history of life on earth; one simply has to rely on observation. Nevertheless, the experiments done in the laboratory are of great help here, and the present tendency is to explain all the observations in terms of what was observed in the laboratory.

2. Processing of the results[2, 6].

The mere gathering of "facts" could be nothing but a hobby. What makes it a science is the systematic processing of these facts. In this processing the facts are categorized and interrelated.

This interrelating is the domain of a theory. In the case where the laws are formulated mathematically, the theory becomes a *mathematical* theory. In a theory one starts from a few *postulates* and interprets a whole body of facts in terms of those postulates. If these postulates are also observed facts, one speaks of a *phenomenological theory*. If the postulates are not observed facts but are introduced to interpret the facts, one speaks of a theory based on a *hypothesis*. The final step is the exposition of the theory and its application to new phenomena.

The reason why the results obtained inside the laboratory can be applied to phenomena outside the laboratory is that the laws of the natural sciences are the same everywhere. The same processes that are at work *now,* also were at work in the *past,* and the same that are at work *here,* are also at work in other parts of the universe. This is known as the *principle of uniformity*. Interpreting phenomena *outside* the laboratory thus means interpretation in terms of *existing* knowledge, usually obtained *in* the laboratory.

This does not always succeed, of course. Sometimes phenomena are encountered that have not yet been duplicated in the laboratory, because the conditions are so radically different from what has been realized in the lab. By simulating those conditions one can often reproduce the phenomena. When that cannot be done, one can often make a good guess how the existing knowledge should be extended so that the phenomena can be understood in terms of this extension. Finally, when even that fails, the new phenomena give at least the first building blocks for a new theory. By searching for additional evidence one may ultimately be able to put the pieces of the puzzle together again.

Applied to the problem of "origin," this means answering the question: "Taking into account the existing laws, from what initial conditions could the present situation have arisen?" The answer is often not unique. True enough, given the laws and the present condition, one can extrapolate back in time. The catch is, however, that one does not always know when to stop, and, as a consequence, one cannot always find a unique set of initial conditions.

3. The certainty of our knowledge[2, 9].

How certain is the knowledge provided by the natural sciences? That depends on the situation.

A "fact" is considered reliable if it has been verified by independent investigators. Wrong observations do occur, of course, but deliberate falsifications are very rare. Independent observations usually correct earlier errors, however, and more detailed investigations result in a modification or an abandonment of a prematurely established law.

What is the situation as far as a theory is concerned? A phenomenological theory has at least some validity. What remains obscure is its *scope*. This can be established by further investigations.

If a clear contradiction is obtained, this does not mean that the theory must be abandoned altogether. Only its limitations have now been shown up. As soon as these limitations are known, one can try to extend the theory in such a manner that the earlier agreements remain intact while the new contingencies are being met.

In other cases, radically new ideas must be introduced to make the theory work. For example, when Maxwell's theory of electromagnetism was applied to the atomic domain, one obtained results that contradicted clear-cut experiments. This led to the discovery of the wave character of matter, which is the basis of the wave-mechanical theory of the atom. No doubt was hereby cast on the applicability of Maxwell's theory to the macroscopic domain.

Sometimes the information at hand is scanty and the assumptions on which the theory is based have not yet been well verified. In such a case it is better to speak of "speculations" than of "hypotheses." One should not be afraid of speculating, for often that is the only way of making real progress. Some of the speculations of today will provide the firm theory of tomorrow. Other speculations, however, will be discarded when better information becomes available.

One should therefore distinguish between facts and well-established hypotheses on the one hand and speculations on the other hand. Often, especially in popular books on science, such a distinction is not made and wild speculations are presented as well-established facts. To avoid this one has to insist on asking the question: "How certain is our knowledge?"

4. The aims of science and of faith.

Science interrelates the phenomena *within* the world around us. It does not try to penetrate into the "nature" of things, but it describes and it interrelates. Faith relates the world around us and ourselves to *God*. That is not the same thing as what science tries to do. For that reason faith should not be seen as an extension of science, nor science as the preliminary of faith.

In the 17th century, science and faith formed a beautiful unity. Science was used to bolster man's faith, and faith was used to illuminate science. Is it surprising that some feel nostalgic when they read how 17th-century scientists managed to blend their science and their faith?

It does not seem possible to do so now. Science could not be contained within the Biblical framework but had to break out of it. Actually, this is a boon, for it throws us back to the question whereon our faith is based. It can then be seen that it is not based upon science but upon Jesus Christ. Science cannot add to it or subtract from it.

This mean, for example, that it is not necessary to use science as a means for developing a powerful apologetics for the existence of God or for the reliability of the Scriptures. The present structure of science is such that it cannot readily supply this kind of apologetics. And the Christian faith does not need this kind of defense. The Biblical message can well stand on its own feet. It does not need *our* support, but we need *its* support.

But this does not mean that science and faith are wholly separated. For faith takes everything around us and relates it to God. And that includes the results of science. For example, the results of science play a part in our praise of the creator. That is not a product of science, however, but it is an act of faith.

REFERENCES AND FURTHER LITERATURE:

[1] C. F. von Weizsäcker, *History of Nature*, Univ. of Chicago Press, 1949.

[2] Aldert van der Ziel, *The Natural Sciences and the Christian Message*, T. S. Denison & Co., Inc., Minneapolis, 1960.

[3] Stanley D. Beck, *The Simplicity of Science*, Penguin Books, Ltd., 1959.

[4] J. B. Conant, *On Understanding Science*, Mentor Books, New York, 1951.

[5] P. W. Bridgman, *The Nature of Physical Theory*, Dover Publications, New York, 1936.

[6] M. Born, *Experiment and Theory in Physics*, Dover Publications, New York, 1956.

[7] P. H. Frank, *Philosophy of Science*, Prentice Hall, Englewood Cliffs, N. J., 1957.

[8] A. d'Arbro, *The Evolution of Scientific Thought*, Dover Publications, New York, 1951.

[9] L. Hutton, *The Language of Modern Physics*, Alan and Unwin, London, McMillan, New York, 1956.

CHAPTER THIRTEEN

The Structure and the Origin
of the Universe

In this chapter we discuss some of the results of modern astronomy, their bearing upon the problem of origins and upon our concept of creation.

1. The structure of the universe[1, 2, 9, 11].

One of the first things one learns from the study of stars is that the distances involved are so huge. For example, the sun is 93,000,000 miles away. For other stars the distances are so huge that they are expressed in *light years*. A star is said to have a distance of one light year if its light must travel one year to reach us. Since light travels with a speed of 186,000 miles per second, a light year is a huge distance. Measured in this unit, the stars in the vicinity of the sun are a few light years apart. Space is thus almost empty.

Our solar system is part of a much larger system of stars: the Milky Way system. This system is a flattened disk of about 60,000 light years in diameter, containing billions of stars. The central part of this system has a long diameter of about 15,000 light years and a short diameter of about 6,500 light years. In the outer regions the stars are arranged in a spiral structure, the so-called spiral arms. Our Milky Way system is therefore a "spiral galaxy." The sun is located in one of the spiral arms at a distance of about 25,000 light years from the center of the galaxy. In the spiral arms are huge gas clouds from which new stars are formed.

The sun is rotating around the center of the galaxy, making one revolution in about 200,000,000 years. The rotation of the galaxy is responsible for its flattened structure and for its spiral arms.

Outside the main disk are globular clusters of stars, each containing about 100,000 stars. Since they are all old stars that are close together, they most likely had a common origin. The star clusters are most numerous near the central part of the disk.

Farther away from our galaxy are other galaxies. Some are of the spiral type, others are more or less elliptic or globular in form and have no spiral arms. Apparently the shape of the galaxies is determined by their speed of rotation. Many of the larger galaxies have globular clusters of stars associated with them. Smaller galaxies may have only 100 million stars, whereas the larger ones may contain up to 10 billion stars.

The galaxies in turn are grouped together in supergalaxies. The supergalaxy to which our galaxy belongs is a flattened structure with a longest diameter of about 40 million light years and a shortest diameter of about 8 million light years. Other supergalaxies have also been found. The total number of galaxies runs into the billions.

The galaxies seem to move away from us with a speed proportional to their distance. Structures have been found that move away from us with a speed almost half the speed of light; they have distances of several billion light years. Extrapolating back into the past, one finds that the galaxies would have been very close together 6-10 billion years ago. This may have some bearing upon the origin of the universe.

2. The life history of a star[4, 7, 20].

Spectroscopic evidence indicates that stars consist mainly of hydrogen, with some helium and traces of other elements added. It is generally agreed that the energy radiated by a star is supplied by fusion of hydrogen into helium through a variety of processes.

A star thus starts as a hydrogen cloud containing traces of other elements. If gravitation predominates over the random motion of its atoms, the star contracts and the interior pressure and temperature build up. Soon the temperature is high enough, so that the star begins to shine. If the interior temperature of the star rises above a few million degrees, fusion reactions start, hydrogen is turned into helium, and huge amounts of energy are generated.

The rate at which energy is generated depends on the mass of the star. Our sun has been shining for about 5 billion years, and the fuel presently available will last for another 5 billion years. The heavier the star, the shorter its life; the heaviest stars can only keep operating for 10-100 million years. They do not live that long, for at a certain stage of their development they will explode.

What will be the future of a star like the sun? When hydrogen is changed into helium, the helium is left behind in the central core of the star. When the helium core grows larger, it also grows hotter. Finally the temperature becomes so high that helium can change into heavier elements in nuclear reactions. This releases so much energy that the star will expand greatly. At this stage of its development the sun will even engulf the inner planets! When the energy generating layer reaches the surface, violent hydrogen explosions (nova explosions) occur, resulting in a large flareup in light intensity for a few weeks. After the star has lost its last hydrogen in a series of such explosions, it will contract greatly toward the so-called white dwarf stage. It has then reached the end of its road.

Much heavier stars than the sun follow the same pattern, but more rapidly. But when the interior temperature reaches about four billion degrees, several processes occur that require so much energy that the pressure balance of the star can no longer be maintained. The star then collapses, the energy-producing outer parts fall into the extremely hot inner parts, and a tremendous explosion, known as a "supernova" explosion occurs. It blows large amounts of material, including heavier elements, into interstellar space.

How do the astronomers know that this is so? There is presently enough theoretical knowledge available to predict the development of a star. And a sufficient number of stars have been studied to verify these predictions. Fantastic as they may seem, the above predictions are reasonably certain.

The universe is in a constant state of flux. New stars are being formed, and old stars become extinguished. Creation is not something that happened once and then stopped, but it is ever continuing.

3. The origin of the universe[5, 6, 7, 12].

As will be seen in the next chapter, the earth is about 4.5 billion years old. There is strong evidence that the solar system is not much older than this. If the extrapolation of the expanding universe is allowed, then the universe should be about 6-10 billion years old. This is the basis of Gamow's "big bang" theory of the universe. According to this theory, the universe started with a tremendous explosion. The larger the speed of the material, the farther it will have receded from the center of the explosion. This explains the expanding universe. But it also explains the galaxies. For small initial disturbances in such a huge system of matter have the tendency to grow. Matter thus condensed first into huge clouds, the beginning of the super-galaxies, these clouds split up into smaller clouds, the beginning of the galaxies, and, finally, the matter of the galaxies condensed into the individual stars.

The difficulty with this theory is that the highly unstable initial condition is left unexplained. It would be more satisfactory if this instability were not needed. For that reason it has been proposed that, while the universe is expanding, new matter is added continuously to keep the average density of matter in the universe constant. This is known as the hypothesis of "continuous creation."

There is presently not enough evidence to decide one way or the other. We still know very little about the universe at large. It is likely that many surprises and discoveries are waiting for us.

Many theories have been proposed for the formation of the solar system. These theories must explain why all these planets move in about the same plane and in the same direction. Several theories do this, but basic difficulties remain.

Recently, the likelihood of life on other planets in our solar system and on planets of other stars has been discussed. The first problem will probably be solved within the next few years, when interplanetary travel becomes possible. There is evidence for low forms of life on Mars. As far as the second problem is concerned, one must have an open mind for the possibilities that life in outer space is either rather common or very rare. We live on the only piece of evidence available to us.

4. Theological conclusions.

Some Christians feel that the theories on the origin of the universe, of our solar system, and of the earth deny the existence of a creator. This objection reflects a mechanistic concept of creation. If it is maintained that creation and natural processes are not contrasts, and that God creates through natural processes, then this objection disappears.

Some Christians object to the idea of a very old earth. They feel that this is in conflict with the Genesis account of creation. It should be pointed out, however, that there is a double conflict, one with geology, and one with astronomy. Geology requires an "old" earth; astronomy requires an "old" universe. This conflict disappears, if it is understood that the word "creation" refers not so much to a *process* as to a *relationship*. We can thus quietly admit to an "old" earth and to an "old" universe and conclude: "Apparently that was the way God created."

We should be willing to accept what astronomy tells us about the birth, life and death of stars, and then conclude: "Apparently that is how God creates." When we see how new stars develop, we can conclude that creation continues.

When God is confessed as creator, it remains sensible to ask what natural processes are involved. The scientist has therefore every right to develop theories on the origin of the universe. He should be allowed to make daring speculations, but he should remember that a speculation is not necessarily a fact. This is sometimes forgotten.

But on the other hand his scientific activity should not prevent a Christian from confessing God as creator. If he knows more, he should confess more. This confession must be made within the framework of today, and for this the results of astronomy are relevant. And when this is done, a Christian can only be astonished how extended and how intricate God's creation is, and how far God's care and love extend into space and time.

But it should be understood that this is a conclusion drawn from faith. The results of science are here approached from the faith in God the creator. This order should not be reversed. A scientist cannot conclude from astronomy that there is a God and that this God cares for him. It is much more likely that he will be lost in space and time and that he will conclude that God, if there is a God, simply does not have the time to be bothered by him. He will most likely end up with the feeling that he is alone in an indifferent and perhaps even hostile universe. This difficulty is overcome, if he *starts* from faith in God the creator and draws his conclusions about the universe from it.

REFERENCES AND FURTHER LITERATURE:

[1] C. F. von Weizsäcker, see Chapter 12.

[2] Aldert van der Ziel, see Chapter 12.

[3] G. Gamow, *Biography of the Earth*, Mentor Books, New York, 1948.

[4] G. Gamow, *Birth and Death of the Sun*, Mentor Books, New York, 1945.

[5] G. Gamow, *The Creation of the Universe*, Mentor Books, New York, 1952.

[6] F. Hoyle, *The Nature of the Universe*, Mentor Books, New York, 1955.

[7] F. Hoyle, *Frontiers of Astronomy*, Mentor Books, New York, 1955.

[8] *The New Astronomy*, A Scientific American Book, Simon & Schuster.

[9] *The Universe*, A Scientific American Book, Simon & Schuster.

[10] A. G. W. Cameron, *Nuclear Astrophysics*, Ann. Review of Nuclear Science, Vol. 8, 299-306, 1958.

[11] G. J. Withrow, *The Structure and Nature of the Universe*, Harper Torch Books, 1959.

[12] Robert Jastrow and A. G. W. Cameron, *Origin of the Solar System*, Academic Press, New York, 1963.

[13] Alexander Koyré, *From the Closed World to the Infinite Universe*, Harper Torch Books, New York.

CHAPTER FOURTEEN

History of the Earth
and of Life on Earth

In this chapter we discuss some results of geology and their bearing upon the history of life on earth. This has consequences for our understanding of the "how" of creation.

1. Geological processes and geological dating[3-4].

Soon after its formation, the earth consisted of molten material with a thin solid crust. When the earth cooled down, the crust gradually grew in thickness. Most of the earth is still kept in a molten state, because decay of radioactive material generates enough heat to prevent the earth from solidifying completely.

Geologists distinguish between *igneous* rocks, which are a consequence of volcanic activity; *sedimentary* rocks, in which the material is deposited by sedimentation; and *metamorphic* rocks, which are rocks of the other two groups that have been modified by large changes in temperature and pressure.

In interpreting the data provided by the geological record, the geologist assumes that the processes responsible in the past are the same ones that are at work now. This is known as the principle of *uniformity*. Some, like volcanic activity, weathering, erosion, and sedimentation, can be observed directly. Other processes, like mountain building by folding of the earth's crust, can be read from the geological record.

The earth must be quite old. Mountain formation, and the wearing down of mountains by weathering and erosion, are very slow processes. They must have been repeated several times before the present condition was achieved. This sets the age of the earth at many million years.

For sedimentary rocks one can determine relative ages with the help of the superposition principle, which considers each layer to be deposited on older layers. In the case of mountain building the sequence may have been disturbed, but it can usually be figured out what the original position was and when the disturbance took place. When the sedimentation has been interrupted by volcanic activity, it can often be figured out when this activity took place.

These methods work over a limited geographical area, but correlation over larger distances can be achieved with the help of fossil studies. This is possible because some animals lived only over a relatively short time so that they are characteristic for a well-defined geological period. They can thus correlate geological formations in widely different geographical areas.

Absolute age determinations can be made for volcanic rocks with the help of radioactive dating techniques. Nuclei of a certain radioactive element decay into nuclei of another element at a certain rate. Knowing this rate, and knowing how much of the radioactive element and of its daughter product are present, one can calculate the age of the rock. The method does not work for sedimentary rocks.

The following decay sequences are available*:

*The number behind each element indicates the number of heavy particles in the nucleus.

a. The uranium-238 lead-206 sequence.

b. The uranium-235 lead-207 sequence.

c. The thorium-232 lead-208 sequence.

d. The rubidium-87 strontium-87 sequence.

e. The potassium-40 argon-40 sequence.

At present these methods give good age determinations for rocks older than a few million years, but it is hoped that the last method can be extended to samples as little as 50,000 years old. This would make an overlap with the carbon-14 method possible, which is used for age determinations below 60,000 years. It will also improve datings in the Pleistocene period. Often the various methods of dating give good agreement. But even if agreement is poor, this is not disastrous, for it can then be decided what geological process was responsible for the discrepancy.

The oldest rocks tested were about 3 billion years old. By measuring many well-dated samples carefully, one can also determine the age of the earth. The most reliable age determination gives about 4.5 billion years.

The geological time scale is usually divided into four periods, each with characteristic forms of life:

Cenozoic (recent life) period (63 million years - date).

Mesozoic (middle life) period (230-63 million years ago).

Paleozoic (ancient life) period (600-230 million years ago).

Cryptozoic (hidden life) period (older than 600 million years).

The most recent part of the Cryptozoic is the Precambrian (1200-600 million years ago).

2. The history of life on earth.

Biologists divide the animal and plant kingdoms into phyla, the phyla into classes, the classes into orders, the orders into families, the families into genera and the genera into species. By determining to what phylum, class, order, etc. a fossil belongs, one may obtain considerable information about the development of life on earth.

The Cryptozoic era is characterized by a relative rarity of fossils, partly because the layers are often seriously disturbed by high temperature and high pressure effects, and partly because the forms of life present at that time could not be well preserved. The oldest fossils (algae) are about 2600 million years old. The earliest worms and sponges date from the Precambrian.

The Paleozoic era is divided into the Cambrian, Ordovician, Silurian, Devonian, Carboniferous and Permian periods. An abundant record of marine life is already available for the Cambrian period. All of a sudden, practically all the animal phyla are present, only the vertebrates are missing from the scene. The earliest fishes date from the Silurian, the earliest amphibians from the Devonian, and the earliest reptiles from the Carboniferous. The first ferns and club mosses date from the Devonian, the first mosses and horsetails from the Carboniferous, and the first gymnosperms date from the same period.

The Mesozoic era consists of the Triassic, Jurassic and Cretaceous periods. It is the era of the dinosaurs. The first primitive birds occur in the Jurassic period. The earliest primitive mammals date from the upper Triassic and the Jurassic periods. The earliest marsupials and insectivores date from the Cretaceous period. The same period sees the first flowering plants (Angiosperms).

The Cenozoic era consists of the tertiary and the quarternary period. Suddenly all the important orders of mammals, including the primates, appear on the scene in the Paleocene and Eocene periods. The quarternary period sees the emergence of man in the Pleistocene. The recent period dates from the last ice age.

Many phyla and classes appear at about the same time. This makes it rather difficult to deduce the development and inter-relationship of the various phyla and classes from the geological record alone (see next chapter).

Undoubtedly a large-scale development of life has taken place. There was a succession of various forms of animal and plant life. Gradually, and in some cases rather suddenly, many more highly developed forms of life appeared and other forms of life disappeared. If one wants to characterize this development by the word "evolution," then this evolution is a well-established fact.

Intermediate forms between the phyla or classes are either rare or nonexistent. This is sometime advanced as an argument in favor of a *creation*. This is a rather dangerous argumentation. The intermediate forms, if they ever existed, could have been rare, so that no traces have yet been found. In addition, the argument reflects a mechanistic concept of creation; creation is here interpreted as a sudden bringing into existence. The Biblical concept of creation is much richer, and should not be degraded.

Some well-meaning Christians have tried to reconcile the "high" ages found by the dating methods with the "low" ages deduced from the Biblical record. They have suggested that the geological strata were created with a "built-in" age. The *measured* age is then equal to the built-in age, whereas the *actual* age is the age given by the Biblical record. This suggestion is a nonsensical contradiction of terms without any justification.

3. Theological conclusions.

When geology started to develop, it was not surprising that the results of geology were linked with the Genesis accounts of creation and of the flood[1, 5]. Those who were active in the field were also firm Christian believers, who accepted the Genesis record as a suitable framework for their science. When geology developed further, it became clear that this framework could not be maintained. Haber[1] gives a good account of the resulting struggle.

One of the early harmonization efforts was to interpret geology in terms of a universal flood. There is indeed sound evidence that the seas penetrated large areas during certain geological periods. But these periods were much earlier than the flood described in Genesis. The Genesis flood must have been a local flood of unusual proportions and not a universal flood.

The whole idea of a universal flood is impossible. If all the water vapor in the air condensed suddenly, then the rainfall would at most be a few feet. And if all the earth were covered with water, and the water evaporated until the atmosphere were saturated, then the water level would only recede by a few feet. Those who argue that this could have been a miracle, must account for a double miracle: one for getting the water here, and one for eliminating it[6].

What made the changeover from the Mosaic time scale to the modern time scale so painful, was the strong tendency toward a natural theology among both the theologians and the scientists. Both believed that the natural sciences could provide needed support for the Biblical revelation. A new view presented by science could thus have strong repercussions in theology. The conflict would have been less painful if science and theology had not been so closely linked.

The study of geology has greatly expanded our horizon as far as past events and past forms of life on earth are concerned. If we approach this knowledge with our Christian faith, we can only be amazed how far God's dominion extends into the past. In unison with Gen. 1 and 2 we must then confess that in all these countless ages God's love and God's care were devoted to His creation and that all the past forms of life were His creatures.

When we see what went on in the past, how the face of the earth changed, and how animal and plant life developed, it is theologically sound to conclude: "Apparently that was the way this world was created by God." Science cannot tell us *that* the world was created by God. But a Christian can learn from science *how* God created the world.

Though the study of geology has changed our view on the world around us, it has not altered our need for confessing God as creator. But since God must be confessed as creator within the framework of today, it has changed the *way* in which that confession is made. Science has provided this framework. For our confession of God as creator the message of Genesis is as binding as ever. But for making this confession understood, the results of science are relevant.

Once again it is important that this order is not reversed. We approach the results of science with our Christian faith and then draw the above conclusions. But if we take the results of science and then draw theological conclusions from them *without* our faith, we do not end up with Christianity. Therefore, we must learn first what Genesis says and then apply this to what science offers.

REFERENCES:

[1]F. C. Haber, *The Age of the World, Moses to Darwin*, The Johns Hopkins Press, Baltimore, 1959 (gives early history of geological chronology).

[2]Aldert van der Ziel, see Chapter 12.

[3]L. T. Aldrich and G. W. Wetherill, *Geochronology by Radioactive Decay*, Ann. Review of Nuclear Science, Vol. 8, 257-298, 1958.

[4]W. F. Libby, *Radiocarbon Dating*, 2d Edition, Univ. of Chicago Press, 1955.

[5]C. C. Gillespie, *Genesis and Geology*, Harper Torch Books, New York, 1959.

[6]H. M. Morris and J. C. Whitcomb, Jr., *The Genesis Flood*, Presb. and Ref. Publishing Co., Philadelphia, 1961 (tries to revive the flood theory of geology).

CHAPTER FIFTEEN

Evolution

In this chapter we discuss certain aspects of the theory of evolution and its bearing upon our concept of creation.

1. The reasons for the evolution controversy.

Of all the issues raised by modern science, none stirred up so much controversy in Christian circles as the theory of evolution. There were several reasons for this:

a. *Religious reasons.* Many Christians saw evolution as a direct attack on cherished beliefs. It was forgotten that the development of natural theology had made Christianity open for such attacks. All too often creation was the biological mechanism by which living beings were given existence. When evolution could give a more detailed explanation of what went on in the past, many biologists abandoned "creationalism" in favor of "evolutionism," and often this meant that the theological concept of creation was abandoned too. If the biological and the theological concepts of creation had not been so closely connected, one would have had the freedom of abandoning "creation" as a biological process while retaining "creation" as a relationship between God and His creatures.

b. *Evolution as a creed.* For many biologists their enthusiasm for evolution was not based upon science, but it sprang from deep convictions. It was a philosophy of life and a view of life. It was a "creed" that was in direct contrast with the Christian creed. To develop such creeds is an interesting enterprise, but it is *not* science. The discussion must be kept within the realm of dispassionate science.

c. *Evolution and natural order.* Many felt that evolution undermined the whole concept of an orderly purposeful universe. They found it difficult to reconcile the tremendous amount of order and structure in the living world with the random forces introduced by the theory of evolution. What was forgotten, was the possibility of a complementary point of view in which evolution and purposeful order are not absolute contrasts but complement each other.

d. *Man's status as "man."* Many were of the opinion that the evolutionists were losing sight of what makes man "man."[6] At a time when the industrial revolution swept over mankind, and man asserted himself as a being of unique capacities, they felt that the evolutionist had lost sight of man's unique position[9]. They were willing to admit that man was part of the animal kingdom, but they were not willing to abandon their view of man's unique position. What was forgotten, was that these two points of view could complement each other.

e. *Man as a descendant from apes.* Many found it repugnant that man should have descended from apes. The evolutionists in the early days had too high an opinion of the degree of certainty of their speculations about man's origin. And the anti-evolutionists forgot that speculations should not be abandoned *in advance.* The judgment should not be based on emotions but should be based on evidence.

The theory of evolution is a scientific theory that needs backing by concrete evidence. If this evidence favors evolution, it will ultimately be accepted as at least *one* aspect of reality. That there may be other aspects to reality is thereby not denied.

2. The evidence for small-scale evolution.

The forces of small-scale evolution are mutations, genetic drift and natural selection. Mutation and genetic drift are *random* forces, whereas natural selection is a *directive* force, aiming at a better adaptation of the species to its environment.

When mutation and genetic drift are seen as random forces, this does not necessarily mean that these processes are governed by chance. The expression either indicates that there are processes at work at a *microscopic* level that cannot be directly observed and described, or that there are processes that cannot be predicted *in advance*.

Modern biology has clarified the processes involved in heredity. It is held that the hereditary characteristics are located in the chromosomes of the nuclei of the animal (or plant) cells and that one or more localized groups of molecules in a chromosome are responsible for a particular hereditary trait. These molecular groups are known as "genes." The hereditary information is coded in the structure of these genes. Changes in the structure give rise to changes in the hereditary characteristics. These changes are known as *mutations*.

With a few exceptions the chromosomes occur in similar pairs. The sex-determining pair in man forms one of these exceptions. In cell multiplication an exact replica is made of each chromosome, then the chromosomes separate to form two nuclei, and finally a cell membrane forms to make two cells.

In the reproductive process a female ovum and a male sperm cell, each containing *half* the number of chromosomes, unite. The chromosomes of the two cells unite to form the nucleus of a new cell that then grows into an animal (or plant). The reduction from the normal number of chromosomes to half that number is achieved when the cell, from which the ovum or sperm cell is derived, divides twice, whereas the chromosomes double only once (meiosis).

In a mating population one speaks of the "gene pool," consisting of all the genes of this population. Because the chromosomes of a given pair show a considerable variability, and because each chromosome pair is randomly reduced to half in the process of meiosis, the gene pool will fluctuate from generation to generation. This is one of the causes of random genetic drift. The term "random genetic drift" refers to any changes in the gene pool by chance events. In large populations these deviations cancel out, in small populations they may not.

Mutations, the changes in the structure of the genes, can occur by thermal agitation of the molecules of the genes or by radiation effects on the gene. The natural mutation rate due to both these processes combined is of the order of 5-50 per million births.

Natural selection is possible, because the total number of offspring of a pair of animals (or plants) is much larger than the number that survives to maturity. There is thus a large premium on changes that make the species better adapted to its environment. If the adaptation is optimized, little can be gained by further changes, but in poorly adapted species natural selection can have a large effect. Sudden changes in the environment that allow further adaptation and optimization are especially important.

Suppose in a certain species a small group breaks away and remains isolated for a long time. Both the main group and the isolated group change because of the combined effects of genetic drift, mutations and natural selection. But in the small isolated group random genetic drift and mutations both have a larger effect. If, after a long time, the two groups come together again, the changes may be so large that interbreeding is no longer possible. The groups then remain side by side as two separate species.

Darwin's finches[4], found on the Galapagos Islands, give a good example of this process. They developed from ancestors that emigrated from the South American mainland. The islands offered ideal opportunities for isolated populations, and as a consequence the single species developed into a number of different species belonging to four different genera.

In the fossil record one also finds examples of well-established lines of descent. For example, the Eohippus of the Eocene period developed via Orohippus, Mesohippus, Merychippus and Pliohippus to the present Equus species: horse, donkey and zebra. As a side development one finds Hipparion and Hypohippus in the Miocene and Hippidium and an extinct Equus species in the Pleistocene. A similar line of descent has been established for the elephants.

All the evidence indicates that a species, though fixed over a relatively short time, does not remain fixed indefinitely. It will change with time, and, if the circumstances are favorable, it may develop into several new species or genera. This part of evolution is well established, and those who want to oppose the concept of evolution, should be careful that they do not reject this part.

3. Evolution of the larger units[3].

What can be said about the evolution of the various phyla and classes? Undoubtedly a large-scale development has taken place. If this development is called evolution, then this too is well established. What remains obscure in most cases is *how* this development has taken place.

The fossil record often does not offer sufficient evidence. For the case of the vertebrates the situation is somewhat better, but the evidence is by no means complete. Further evidence comes from comparative embryology. Since the species of a certain line of development have genes in common, the embryonic stages of each species will have some resemblance to the embryonic stages of their ancestors. When the embryo develops, the species depart progressively from each other. Embryology thus gives information about the path of evolution.

Evolution sees the relationship between the larger units in the animal and the plant kingdoms at a genetic relationship, as a descent of complicated forms from simpler ones. It sees the living world as a unity and ties all the myriad forms of animal and plant life together. Since the evidence is more indirect than in the case of the evolution of the smaller units, the opposition can be more outspoken. But is it wise to be so critical? Either one sees the living world as a unity, or it falls apart into a large number of unrelated units. For those with a systematic mind the choice is clear.

This idea of evolution is not a contradiction to the idea of creation. For it sees the species existing at a given point as the starting stage for new animal and plant forms. One must only be willing to admit that the actual course of creation must be read from the biological record rather than from the Bible.

By what mechanisms did evolution take place? Here the opinions are divided. Some feel that new processes must be postulated to account for large-scale evolution. The Neo-Darwinists think that the processes causing small-scale evolution are sufficient. Theologians do wise to leave this question to the experts.

4. The origin of life.

Careful experiments have indicated that "spontaneous generation" of life from lifeless forms does not occur in the present world. Life, as we know it, comes from life. But since the earth was first lifeless, there must have been a time in the history of the earth when life came from lifeless forms. How did this come about? The answer to this question is necessarily speculative.

Living matter is made up of protein molecules, which, in turn, consist of amino acids. Careful experiments have indicated that these amino acids could have arisen in the primeval atmosphere of the earth. The fundamental building blocks would thus have been available quite early, and they could have aggregated into more complex molecules. Whether genes and chromosomes could have been formed that way is another question. The complexity of present living matter is staggering.

Living matter reproduces itself. Perhaps early forms of life reproduced differently from present forms. Early reproduction might perhaps have come by means of "self-catalysis"; this is a chemical process where each molecule is its own catalyst. Similar molecules could therefore have been growing from the building blocks found in their environment. This might have given very primitive forms of life.

Life is built on energy. In the present forms of life, photosynthesis and respiration occur. In the first process, carbon dioxide and water, under the influence of light, give glucose and free oxygen. In respiration, glucose is transformed into carbon dioxide and water by oxidation, and energy is released. In the early atmosphere there was apparently no free oxygen and perhaps also no free carbon dioxide, so that the photosynthesis-respiration cycle was not possible. Other processes must be invoked that could have provided the carbon dioxide needed to start this cycle.

For a fuller discussion of current thinking on the origin of life the reader is referred to the literature[1, 3, 8].

5. Theological conclusions.

The dilemma "creation or evolution" is a false one [11, 12, 13]. If the biological evidence requires that a Christian accepts evolution, he should willingly do so. His faith in the creator is not based on biological evidence, and hence, it cannot be shaken by it. He can leave the question about the scope and the validity of the theory of evolution to the experts. Or, if he is an expert himself, he can follow the quest for truth wherever it may lead him. The evidence cannot change the "that" of creation, it can only change his views on the "how" of creation. Creation and evolution are not contrasts, but they complement each other.

Some Christians feel that the evidence for creation can be read directly from the record of purposeful design, so that creation becomes a conclusion of science. Unfortunately, this faith in the creator is now subjected to corrections necessitated by further evidence. The Biblical concept of creation does not suffer this fate.

The theory of evolution clarifies the Christian concept of creation. If a Christian's view of creation is a mechanistic one, then the theory of evolution shows him the error of his thinking. If his faith in the creator is based on purposeful design arguments, then the theory shows him the weakness of the ground upon which his faith rests. If his concept of creation does not allow for the possibility of evolution, then it is too restricted, and he is robbing God of His freedom.

For some biologists the theory of evolution is a creed, upon which a whole system of values is built. That is a misuse of science. Though a Christian is justified in attacking this misuse, he should not carry the attack into the biological domain. For he is not against the theory of evolution, he is only against its misuse [12, 13]. By attacking the theory of evolution as such, one creates the false impression that the Christian faith is based upon the invalidity of the theory. It should be made quite clear that this is not the case.

REFERENCES AND FURTHER LITERATURE:

[1]D. J. Merrell, *Evolution and Genetics*, Holt, Rinehart and Winston, New York, 1962.

[2]Bernhard Rensch, *Evolution Above the Species Level*, Columbia Univ. Press, 1960.

[3]Sol Tax (Editor), *Evolution After Darwin, Vol. 1, The Evolution of Life; Vol. 2, The Evolution of Man; Vol. 3, Issues in Evolution*, University of Chicago Press, 1960.

[4]David Lack, *Darwin's Finches*, Harper Torch Books, New York.

[5]F. C. Haber, see Chapter 14.

[6]A. Portmann, *Biologische Fragmente zu einer Lehre vom Menschen*, B. Schwabe and Co., Basel, 1951. Reprinted as: *Zoologie und das neue Weltbild vom Menschen*, Rowohlt, Hamburg, 1956.

[7]Stanley D. Beck, see Chapter 12.

[8]A. I. Oparin, *The Origin of Life*, Dover Publications, New York, 1953.

[9]Karl Barth, *Kirchliche Dogmatik*, Vol. III. 2, Evangelischer Verlag, A. G. Zollikon/Zürich, 1948 (references to the theological opposition against Darwinistic anthropology).

[10]David Lack, *Evolutionary Theory and Christian Belief*, Methuen, 1957.

[11]Jan Lever, *Creation and Evolution*, Grand Rapids Int. Publications, 1958. (A good discussion from a conservative Christian background.)

[12]Paul A. Zimmermann, *Darwin, Evolution and Creation*, Concordia, St. Louis, 1959.

[13]John W. Klotz, *Genes, Genesis and Evolution*, Concordia, St. Louis, 1955.

(The last two authors take an overcritical attitude toward the problem.)

CHAPTER SIXTEEN

The History of Man
and of Man's Ancestry

Chapters 14 and 15 described the development of life on earth, but did not deal with the development of man. That problem is discussed in this chapter.

1. The fossil record.

The best known fossil finds of early man can be listed as follows:

> The ice age man, 100,000 - 10,000 years ago.
>
> Neanderthal man, 150,000 - 60,000 years ago.
>
> Peking man, 400,000 - 250,000 years ago.
>
> Chellian-3 man, about 400,000 years ago.
>
> Java man, about 500,000 years ago.
>
> *Homo habilis,* about 2 million years ago.

A large number of related finds have been reported. For a good list see Coon[11].

Recently, some of these early remains have been given new Latin names, to reflect changes in the opinions about their kinship to man[11]. The ice age man is now considered to be *Homo sapiens,* modern man. Neanderthal man was first named

Homo neanderthalensis. He is now named *Homo sapiens nean-derthalensis*, indicating that he is considered to be a subspecies of modern man. Early European forms of *Homo sapiens* are a few hundred thousand years old.

The Peking man and Java man were first named *Sinan-thropus pekinensis* and *Pithecanthropus erectus*, respectively, indicating that they belonged to different genera differing from *Homo*. At present they are considered to be subspecies or races of *Homo erectus*, so that a much closer kinship is assumed. Chellian-3 man, discovered in 1960 by Leakey[4] at Olduvai gorge (Tanganyika) belongs to the African form of *Homo erectus*.

In South Africa, Dart and Broom found many skulls of man-like creatures, which they placed in the group Australopithe-cinae. Initially this group was classified into four genera and six species, but it is now held that the group as a whole was no more variable than the living chimpanzee[11]. In 1959-1960 Leakey discovered a man-like skull in Olduvai gorge, to which he gave the name *Zinjanthropus boiseii*. At first he thought *Zinjanthropus* might be an ancestor of man, but it is presently believed that he belongs to the Australopithecinae, with which he was contemporary.

In 1961 Leakey[4] found part of the skull of a child which he named pre-Zinjanthropus. In 1964 similar finds were re-ported. It is now held that these fossils are much closer to mod-ern man than *Zinjanthropus*, and for that reason the name *Homo habilis* has been proposed. *Homo habilis* is probably about 2 million years old, but this age is still somewhat in doubt[11].

Before going on, we must deal for a moment with zoologi-cal nomenclature. Man belongs to the mammalian order of Primates. Man and apes belong to the superfamily Hominoidea, which is divided into three families: Hylobatidae (gibbon, siamang), Pongidae (orangutan, chimpanzee, gorilla) and Hominidae (man). A hominid is thus man-like, not ape-like, and is characterized by an erect posture. Hominoids may either be man-like or ape-like and may or may not have erect posture.

The Australopithecinae are definitely hominid. But if one goes farther back into the past, it becomes more and more difficult to decide whether or not the fossils should be classified as true hominid. This is not surprising, for one would expect the hominids to have originated from nonhominid ancestors. Some early finds that may lead to true hominids are listed below[2, 3, 4, 9, 11]:

Oreopithecus bamboli, found in Italy, and about 10 million years old[11]. Some consider him to belong to the group of species that included the ancestors of man. According to others, *Oreopithecus* was an ape.

Kenyapithecus wickeri, about 14 million years old[4]. The structure of the upper jaw suggests many human features, including perhaps the potentiality of speech.

Ramapithecus, found in northwest India, and about 10 million years old[3]. He also had many man-like features.

The order of Primates is very old[2, 3]. Early primate fossils date from at least the lower Eocene and are about 50 million years old. Hominoids are also found quite early. Gibbons separated from the early hominoids at least 35 million years ago. *Proconsul,* about 25 million years old, shows some man-like and some ape-like features and may have been a forerunner of both apes and man. Others think, however, that he represents a separate evolutionary line. The fossil genera *Dryopithecus* and *Sivapithecus,* about 20 million years old, resemble the great apes.

It is presently held that man did not descend from the anthropoid apes, but that both had common ancestors. It is held that the separation between the true apes and the true hominids occurred quite early. The same conclusion can be drawn from the fact that the biological gap between the anthropoid apes and man is quite large (Portmann[6]).

The remains of *Homo habilis* give clear evidence for the existence of the genus *Homo* about 2 million years ago. The relationship between *Homo habilis* and *Homo erectus* needs further clarification. *Homo erectus* is considered to be the true ancestral species of modern man. Coon[11] believes that the races of *Homo erectus* evolved individually into the races of modern man. Peking man evolved into the Mongoloid race, Java man evolved into the Australoid race and the European and African representatives of *Homo erectus* evolved into the Caucasoid race and the Negroid race, respectively.

2. Development of man's intellectual and cultural capacities.

What sets man apart from the other animals is his intelligence and his ability to receive and transmit culture. This is a consequence of the development of man's brain. This development is reflected in the cranial capacities of man's ancestors.

Table I. Cranial capacities of hominids and pongids.

Modern man — 900-2100 cm^3

Neanderthal man — 1200-1650 cm^3

Peking man — 900-1200 cm^3

Java man — 775-950 cm^3

Homo habilis — 700 cm^3

Australopithecinae — 450-600 cm^3

Zinjanthropus — 530 cm^3

Anthropoid apes — 325-700 cm^3

The accompanying table[11] compares the cranial capacities of man and his ancestors with those of the anthropoid apes and the Australopithecinae. It shows that a great increase in cranial capacity has taken place. This probably indicates a corresponding increase in man's intelligence, that is, in his ability to think, to reason, to communicate and to develop and transmit culture.

The two important anatomic features of man are his erect posture and his brain development. Fossil evidence seems to indicate that erect posture was developed first and that the increase in brain development came later.

Man's cultural development reflects itself in the use of stone tools. Leakey found stone tools of the "Oldowan" culture at Olduvai gorge on the same living floor where *Zinjanthropus* was found, and found indications of rough shelters or windbreaks in contemporary layers in the vicinity. These were at first attributed to *Zinjanthropus,* but the discovery of *Homo habilis* has changed the picture. Leakey and his associates write[5]: "The subsequent discovery of the remains of *Homo habilis* in association with the Oldowan culture at three other sites has considerably altered the position. While it is possible that *Zinjanthropus* and *Homo habilis* both made stone tools, it is probable that the latter was the more advanced tool maker and that the *Zinjanthropus* skull represents an intruder (or a victim) on a *Homo habilis* living site."

There is some, but inconclusive, evidence for the use of stone tools among the Australopithecinae. The same can now be said about *Zinjanthropus.*

The earliest stone tools were probably used mostly for skinning animals[4]. Later more sophisticated stone tools and actual stone weapons came into use. Man was first an unskilled hunter, killing only relatively small animals. But gradually his hunting skills developed and he became able to kill large animals. According to Leakey[4], Chellean-3 man was already a skilled hunter. The first clear-cut evidence for the use of fire is found among Peking man, but it is suspected that fire was used much earlier.

In the agricultural revolution, which started about 10,000 years ago, man acquired the skills of farming and animal husbandry; he thereby became a food *producer* rather than a food *gatherer*. Living in small agricultural villages became common. Still later the urban revolution occurred; man became a city dweller and agriculture was joined by industry. Early economy and early forms of government developed. What is considered to be the dawn of recorded history was thereby reached.

3. Theological conclusions.

It is sometimes held that the study of man's ancestry is detrimental to the Christian faith. This is a misunderstanding. The certainty of the Christian faith does not lie in man's ancestry, but it lies in Jesus Christ.

It is sometimes held that the results of the study of man's ancestry contradict the Genesis account of creation. This too is a misunderstanding. The Genesis account stresses that God is creator of all that is. The findings about man's ancestry only mean that our concept of creation must be extended. The more we learn about the past history of man, the more forms of human-like life must be confessed as being created by God.

According to our discussion of Genesis 2, 3, and 5, it is theologically relevant to see Adam as our representative, as the

first man, as the first sinner, as the first in a long line of believers. Theologically speaking, Adam is the "father of mankind," just as Abram is the "father of believers." From our
present state of knowledge about man's ancestry, the idea of a
"first man" seems to be neither biologically nor historically
relevant, however.

As long as the theological significance of Adam is stressed
to the fullest extent, the biological and historical identity of
Adam remains a matter of secondary importance. If it is stressed,
one runs into difficulties with the prehistoric record. If it is
denied, one should watch out that the theological significance
of Adam is not eliminated at the same time.

REFERENCES AND FURTHER LITERATURE:

[1]Sol Tax (Editor). *Evolution After Darwin, Vol. 2, The Evolution of Man*,
Univ. of Chicago Press, 1960.

[2]D. J. Merrell, see Chapter 15.

[3]Gabriel W. Lasker, *The Evolution of Man*, Holt, Rinehart and Winston, New
York, 1961.

[4]L. S. B. Leakey on *Zinjanthropus* etc., *National Geographic*, Sept. 1960, Oct.
1961, Jan. 1963.

[5]L. S. B. Leakey and others on *Homo habilis*, etc., *Nature*, Vol. 202, April 4,
pp. 3-9, 1964.

[6]A. Portmann, see Chapter 15.

[7]A. Portmann, *Vom Ursprung des Menschen*, F. Reinhardt, Basel, 1944.

[8]Pierre Teilhard de Chardin, *The Phenomenon of Man*, Harper Torch Books,
New York, 1961.

[9]L. S. B. Leakey, *Adam's Ancestors, The Evolution of Man and His Culture*,
Harper Torch Books, New York, 1960.

[10]Carleton S. Coon, *The History of Man*, J. Cape, London, 1962.

[11]Carleton S. Coon, *The Origin of Races*, Alfred A. Knopf, Inc., New York,
1962.

[12]Jan Lever, see Chapter 15.

CHAPTER SEVENTEEN

Conclusion

1. Discrepancies between science and Genesis?

We can now answer the question whether there are discrepancies between science and Genesis. There is none, if the proper distinction is made between the *message* of Genesis and the framework of the ancient world view. There are plenty of discrepancies if this distinction is not made. Let us examine some of them in more detail.

1. The distant past seems to give no indication that animal life was once exclusively vegetarian. Animal life feeding on animal life was quite common even in the distant past. This seems to conflict with the vegetarian existence of animals and man in Gen. 1 (and later in Isaiah 11). It should be noted, however, that this is a *theological* reference to a creation that is not yet (or no longer) spoiled by human sin. It is not a *biological* reference. "Nature red of tooth and claw" is not a *consequence* of human sin, it is at most a *symbol* of human sin.*

---

*Contrary to what Alan Richardson (l. c.) seems to suggest.

2. The distant past seems to give no indication of a "first" man, in contrast with Gen. 2 and 3. We saw, when going back in time, that it became increasingly difficult to decide in how far the beings under consideration were "human." Extrapolating back into the past, one thus comes into a no-man's land of seemingly unlimited extent. Theologically speaking, the "first" man was introduced in Gen. 2 and 3 to confess that sin goes to man's very beginning. He was not introduced because of paleontological interests.

3. There seems to be no indication of an idyllic beginning during which man lived in a state of innocence. This is in contrast with Gen. 2. As a matter of fact, paleontology teaches what Gen. 4 teaches: that man has been a murderer from his very beginning. The idyllic beginning of Gen. 2 was introduced to deny that God is the author of sin and to emphasize that man is responsible for his sin. It was not introduced because of paleontological interests, once again.

4. There seems to be no indication that early man grew very old. On the contrary, paleontological evidence indicates that man died relatively young. In view of the harsh conditions of human existence in those days, this is not too surprising. The longevity of the patriarchs in Gen. 5 and Gen. 11 was not introduced as a biological curiosity but it aimed at bringing a message of theological intent (Chapter 7).

We said: "There seems to be no indication . . ." These words were chosen carefully. The possibility can never be fully excluded that some of our scientific views may change in view of new evidence. All that can be said here is: "that is how things look to us at present." One cannot predict the future course of science.

As said before, these discrepancies disappear if the proper distinction is made between the message and the framework. The message has a theological intent and content. The main themes of the Biblical message are not touched by science. God is creator, and that cannot be proved or disproved by science. Man is a sinner and God punishes and forgives sin. That again is outside the realm and the competence of science. God rules over everything and all the world is His domain. That once more is not proved or disproved by science, but it is something that must be *preached* and *believed*. And so we could go on.

There are, of course, certain attitudes that can only lead to conflict. Some maintain: "The Bible is God's word and it is true. If science teaches something in conflict with what the Bible teaches, then science has to give." Others say: "Science stands for truth, and if the Bible teaches something contrary to science, then the Bible has to give." Both lead to conflict, since both take a monistic attitude and refuse to distinguish between the message and the framework. Let us look at these attitudes in more detail.

The first say: "The Bible is God's word," and with this we agree. They add: "The Bible is true," and that again is correct. But here it must be asked: "True in what respect?" The answer must be: "True as far as the message is concerned." It cannot mean: "True as far as the framework is concerned." Since the message had to be brought *within* the existing framework of its time in order to be heard, it is the *message* that counts and *not* the framework. But if that is understood, then it is no longer true that science teaches something in conflict with what the Bible teaches: there is then, at most, conflict with the ancient framework. Consequently, nothing has to give, but science and the message can stand side by side.

The other side says: "Science stands for truth," and that is correct. But this does not mean that we are in the "possession" of truth. We *strive* for truth, we continue to make progress toward truth, but we have not *reached* our goal. Moreover, there is not *one* truth, there are *many* truths. The truth that two times two makes four and the truth that God is my creator are not on the same level. They are different and they should be *distinguished*. Once the possibility of the "many" truths has been admitted and the distinction between the message and the framework has been made, the so-called conflicts between science and the Bible cease to be burning questions.

The solution to most of the seeming conflicts between science and the Bible thus lies in the distinction between the message and the framework. This distinction is essential; if it is not made, one is courting serious trouble.

2. The role of critical Biblical scholarship.

In the exegetic part of this book the results of critical Old Testament scholarship were used freely. This was done to demonstrate that this method can be put to good use and that it is unnecessary to be afraid of it. The aim of the method is not to *destroy* the message, but instead it aims at *getting at* the message. It insists on asking for and looking for the *theological* content of the text.

By doing so, the method automatically distinguishes between the message and the framework. And for that reason it helps in avoiding conflicts between science and the Biblical message. The theological and the scientific views presented in this book thus *complement* each other.

Of course, one can make the proper distinction between the message and the framework without adopting the results of critical Old Testament scholarship. All that is needed is that one insists on asking for the *theological* content of the text. The method of critical Old Testament scholarship provides *one* approach, but this is not necessarily the only one. The results of this method can be used carefully and thankfully; they should not be used slavishly. The theologian is *free,* also in this respect.

That does not mean that *all* methods of approach are equally useful. Some lead to confusion and should be avoided. All methods that help understanding the Biblical message and that avoid conflicts with science are useful. All methods that invite conflicts with science are harmful.

There is one particular attitude that is very harmful for the relationship between theology and science. We illustrate it from the following two quotations[4]:

"While it is true that the Bible is not a textbook of science, yet if its scientific statements are found to be false, it is difficult to see how we may retain confidence in its divine inspiration even of the spiritual truths which it contains."

"Jesus Christ rested weighty matters upon quotations from the books of Moses, and always referred to them as authoritative and true. If His attitude were wrong, then all belief in His deity must be given up, and the very foundation of Christianity discarded."

In the same vein one could go on. Some well-meaning Christians seem to maintain that Jesus is not the Christ, the Son of God, unless Adam was the first man, unless Abel really existed, unless Moses wrote the first five books of the Bible, or unless Jonah was really swallowed by the whale. We want to state *most emphatically* that the question whether or not Jesus was the Christ, the Son of God, is completely independent of those questions. To maintain the contrary is bad logic and poor theology.

3. Science and our concept of creation.

The Bible tells us that the world is God's creation. Science tells us what is *in* this world and it tries to find out how everything came about. We may thus state that the Bible teaches the "that" of creation and that science informs us about the "when" and the "how" of creation. The Bible and science can thus complement each other and science helps shaping our concept of creation.

a. According to the Bible, the statement "God creates" means: "God brings into existence and gives this existence a meaning, a purpose and a future." Because God created me, life is not meaningless. Because God created me, life has a purpose: to serve and glorify him (Gen. 1). Because God created me, life has a future, despite what I have done (Gen. 3).

b. According to the Bible, creation is not "beginning" in the broad sense of the word, but it means: "God began" (Gen. 1:1). The most important fact is not that there *was* a beginning, but that *God began.*

c. According to the Bible, creation does not consist of setting initial conditions and then letting go. That is deism. Creation encompasses all that exists, happens and goes on.

d. According to the Bible, creation is not "explanation" of the world around us, but it relates this world, and the things in this world, to God. "Explanations" can be quietly left to the domain of science, but the relationship between God and this world is eminently the domain of theology.

e. The Biblical concept of creation does not coincide with

our concept of "sudden appearance." Creation should therefore not be invoked to explain the sudden appearance of new
species in the animal or plant kingdom. That God is creator,
is independent of the suddenness or the graduality with which
new species appear. Once again, creation "relates," it does not
"explain."

f. Creation is not "manufacturing." It is true that Gen. 2
seems to equate creation with manufacturing, but that is done
to express a very particular relationship between the man, the
animals and the field. Hence, creation should not be equated
to a biological process.

g. Creation has a *purpose,* but the concept of creation
should not be identified with "purposeful design." Modern biology probably does not take enough notice of "purposeful
structure" at present, but past experience has taught biologists
to be very sceptical about purposeful design arguments. Their
fascination with random (= purposeless) phenomena can be
seen as a reaction to a previous overemphasis of those arguments. Wherever the truth may lie in this question, the fact
remains that purposeful design arguments are not very popular
and should be used with great caution.

h. According to the Bible, creation and natural processes
are not contrasts, but go hand in hand (Gen. 1). God creates
in and through the natural order. Looking at things from a
scientific point of view, the natural processes extend all the
way; looking at the same things from a theological point of
view, God's creative activity extends all the way. The two points
of view thus complement each other.

i. Creation and evolution are not contrasts[6, 7]. We can
freely admit the possibility that God can create through evolutionary processes. And we can leave the ultimate fate of the

theory of evolution in the hands of the experts. That God is creator, is independent of whether the theory of evolution is true, false, or merely incomplete.

j. Creation and random processes are not contrasts either. What *we* label as "random," is for that reason not outside God's control. But God's control is not a fact that we can read from the record. It is the *faith* with which we approach the record. We *believe* that everything is under God's control.

k. Creation is not tied to a deterministic universe. A universe describable by random processes coupled to natural selection may have many more possibilities for future development than a deterministic universe. Why should not God have the freedom to *use* such a flexible universe to carry out His creative will?

l. Creation is not tied to our lack of knowledge. God is not only the creator of those things that we do not understand yet. If that were the case, then God's domain would shrink when the domain of our knowledge and understanding expands. God is not a "gap-stopper." Even if we would know everything, God should still be confessed as the creator of all.

m. As said before, that God creates is not read from the biological or geological record. Rather, it is the *faith* with which the record is approached. As in Gen. 1 and in John 1, creation is for us a conclusion of faith.

4. Our Christian task as scientists[1].

Scientists, who are also Christians, have a double task. In the first place, they have an obligation to their science: to work in it faithfully and to maintain a positive but critical attitude toward it. According to Gen. 1, that is their God-given task[5].

In the second place they have an obligation to the church: to enlighten the members in general and the clergy in particular about the results and the attitudes of modern science. They thus provide the background against which the Christian message is placed.

Some well-meaning Christians are so eager to defend the integrity of the Bible, that they are willing to misrepresent science. Up to a certain point their discussion is fully objective. But when it comes to problems like the age determination of rocks, man and the earth, or the problem of evolution, they all of a sudden become overcritical. They try to create the impression that the age determinations are largely unreliable and that the arguments against evolution are much stronger than those in its favor. By doing so, they misrepresent the truth and create a false security[6,7].

On the other hand, some are so eager to be modern and up to date that they are willing to abandon large parts of the Biblical message as unessential. What remains is perhaps better palatable to some, but it lacks power.

The answer to these difficulties is to let science and the Biblical message stand side by side without eliminating parts of the one or the other. It should be attempted to delineate as clearly as possible where each one stands for. It will then be seen that seemingly insoluble conflicts disappear. To bring this about is the Christian task of the scientists in the church. Our attempt made in this book should be seen as a modest contribution to this effort.

REFERENCES AND FURTHER LITERATURE:

[1]Aldert van der Ziel, see Chapter 12.

[2]Stanley D. Beck, see Chapter 12.

[3]Otto Schuepp, *Schöpfungsbericht und Naturwissenschaft*, Reinhardt, Basel,

[4]*Modern Science and Christian Faith*, Van Kampen Press, Wheaton, Ill., 1948.

[5]John W. Klotz, *Modern Science in the Christian Life*, Concordia, St. Louis, 1961.

[6]John W. Klotz, see Chapter 15.

[7]Paul A. Zimmermann, see Chapter 15.

Authors Index

Index